Bond

Maths

Assessment Papers

9-10 years

Book 1

OXFORD
UNIVERSITY PRESS

Great Clarendon Street, Oxford, OX2 6DP, United Kingdom

Oxford University Press is a department of the University of Oxford.
It furthers the University's objective of excellence in research, scholarship,
and education by publishing worldwide. Oxford is a registered trade mark of
Oxford University Press in the UK and in certain other countries

British Library Cataloguing in Publication Data
Data available

978-0-19-274014-4

10 9 8 7 6 5 4 3 2 1

Paper used in the production of this book is a natural, recyclable
product made from wood grown in sustainable forests.
The manufacturing process conforms to the environmental
regulations of the country of origin.

Printed in China

Acknowledgements

The publishers would like to thank the following for permissions to
use copyright material:

Page make-up: OKS Prepress, India
Illustrations: Tech-Set Limited
Cover illustrations: Lo Cole

Although we have made every effort to trace and contact all
copyright holders before publication this has not been possible in all
cases. If notified, the publisher will rectify any errors or omissions at
the earliest opportunity.

Links to third party websites are provided by Oxford in good faith
and for information only. Oxford disclaims any responsibility for
the materials contained in any third party website referenced in
this work.

Before you get started

What is Bond?

This book is part of the Bond Assessment Papers series for maths, which provides **thorough and continuous practice of all the key maths content** from ages five to thirteen. Bond's maths resources are ideal preparation for many different kinds of tests and exams – from SATs to 11+ and other secondary school selection exams.

What does this book cover and how can it be used to prepare for exams?

It covers all the maths that a child of this age would be expected to learn and is fully in line with the National Curriculum for maths and the National Numeracy Strategy. *Maths 9-10 Book 1* and *Book 2* can be used both for general practice and as part of the run up to 11+ exams, Key Stage 2 SATs and other selective exams. One of the key features of Bond Assessment Papers is that each one practises **a wide variety of skills and question types** so that children are always challenged to think – and don't get bored repeating the same question type again and again. We think that variety is the key to effective learning. It helps children 'think on their feet' and cope with the unexpected.

What does the book contain?

- **24 papers** – each one contains 50 questions.
- **Tutorial links throughout** – [B 7] – this icon appears in the margin next to the questions. It indicates links to the relevant section in *How to do ... 11+ Maths*, our invaluable subject guide that offers explanations and practice for all core question types.
- **Scoring devices** – there are score boxes in the margins and a Progress Chart on page 64. The chart is a visual and motivating way for children to see how they are doing. It also turns the score into a percentage that can help decide what to do next.
- **Next Steps Planner** – advice on what to do after finishing the papers can be found on the inside back cover.
- **Answers** – located in an easily-removed central pull-out section.

How can you use this book?

One of the great strengths of Bond Assessment Papers is their flexibility. They can be used at home, in school and by tutors to:

- set **timed formal practice** tests – allow about 30 minutes per paper. Reduce the suggested time limit by five minutes to practise working at speed.
- provide **bite-sized chunks** for regular practice.
- highlight **strengths and weaknesses** in the core skills.

- identify **individual needs**.

- set **homework**.

- follow a complete 11+ preparation strategy alongside *The Parents' Guide to the 11+* (see below).

It is best to start at the beginning and work through the papers in order. Calculators should not be used.

Remind children to check whether each answer needs a unit of measurement before they start a test. If units of measurement are not included in answers that require them, they will lose marks for those questions. To ensure that children can practise including them in their answers, units of measurement have been omitted after the answer rules for some questions.

If you are using the book as part of a careful run-in to the 11+, we suggest that you also have two other essential Bond resources close at hand:

How to do ... 11+ Maths: the subject guide that explains the question types practised in this book. Use the cross-reference icons to find the relevant sections.

The Parents' Guide to the 11+: the step-by-step guide to the whole 11+ experience. It clearly explains the 11+ process, provides guidance on how to assess children, helps you to set complete action plans for practice and explains how you can use *Maths 9-10 Book 1* and *Book 2* as part of a strategic run-in to the exam.

See the inside front cover for more details of these books.

What does a score mean and how can it be improved?

It is unfortunately impossible to predict how a child will perform when it comes to the 11+ (or similar) exam if they achieve a certain score on any practice book or paper. Success on the day depends on a host of factors, including the scores of the other children sitting the test. However, we can give some guidance on what a score indicates and how to improve it.

If children colour in the Progress Chart on page 64, this will give an idea of present performance in percentage terms. The Next Steps Planner inside the back cover will help you to decide what to do next to help a child progress. It is always valuable to go over wrong answers with children. If they are having trouble with any particular question type, follow the tutorial links to *How to do ... 11+ Maths* for step-by-step explanations and further practice.

Don't forget the website ...!

Visit www.bond11plus.co.uk for lots of advice, information and suggestions on everything to do with Bond, the 11+ and helping children to do their best.

Key words

Some special maths words are used in this book. You will find them **in bold** each time they appear in the papers. These words are explained here.

acute angle an angle that is less than a right angle

edge the line where two faces join

face a flat side of a solid object

factor the factors of a number are numbers that divide into it, for example 1, 2, 4 and 8 are all factors of 8

improper fraction a fraction with the numerator bigger than the denominator

lowest term the simplest you can make a fraction, for example $\frac{4}{10}$ reduced to the lowest term is $\frac{2}{5}$

mean one kind of average. You find the mean by adding all the scores together and dividing by the number of scores, for example the mean of 1, 3 and 8 is 4

median one kind of average, the middle number of a set of numbers after being ordered from lowest to highest, for example the median of 1, 3 and 8 is 3

mixed number a number that contains a whole number and a fraction, for example $5\frac{1}{2}$ is a mixed number

mode one kind of average. The most common element in a set of data, for example the mode of 2, 3, 2, 7, 2 is 2

obtuse angle an angle that is more than 90° and not more than 180°

polygon a closed shape with three or more sides

range the difference between the largest and smallest of a set of numbers, for example the range of 1, 2, 5, 3, 6, 8 is 7

reflex angle an angle that is bigger than 180° and less than 360°

scalene triangle three-sided polygon with no two sides of the same length

vertex, vertices the point where two or more edges or sides in a shape meet

Paper 1

What fraction of each shape is shaded or dotted?

1

Shaded $\frac{1}{2}$ ✓

2

Shaded $\frac{1}{2}$ ✓

3

Shaded $\frac{16}{8}$ ✓

4

Dotted $\frac{1}{2}$ ✓

5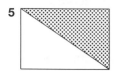

Dotted $\frac{1}{2}$ ✓

6

Dotted $\frac{1}{4}$ ✓

7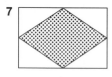

Dotted $\frac{1}{2}$ ✓

8

Shaded $\frac{1}{2}$ ✓

B 10

8

Put a sign in each space so that each question will be correct.

9–10 $(3 \; < \; 4) \; > \; 4 = 8$ ✗

11–12 $(5 \; < \; 4) \; > \; 4 = 24$ ✗

B2/B3

4

13–15 What numbers will come out of the machine?

B 9

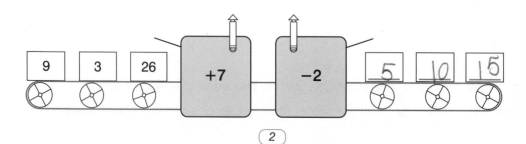

3

16–20 Reflect these figures in the lines of symmetry.

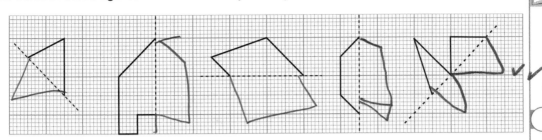

✓✓✓✓✓

5

Here is a bar chart to show which colours we like.

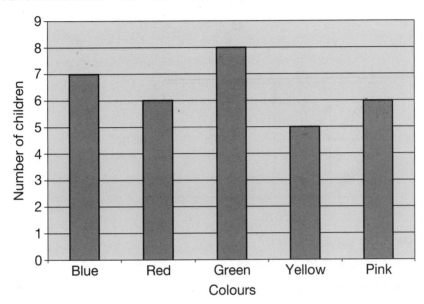

21 How many children are there in our class?

22 What colour is the **mode**?

23 What colour is the least popular?

24–25 Which two colours are equally popular?

Half of those who like green are boys.

Half of those who like red are girls.

One boy likes pink.

Six boys like blue.

Three girls like yellow.

26 How many boys are in the class?

27 How many girls are in the class?

32 ✓

8 ✗

5

<u>red</u> and <u>pink</u> ✓

15 ✗

17 ✗   7

I think of a number. I double it. I then add 5.

28 The answer is 7. What was the number?

1 ✓   1

3

Write the next two numbers in each of the following lines.

29–30	800	400	200	100	50	25 ✓✓
31–32	9	12	15	18	21	24 ✓ ∫
33–34	55	50	45	40	35	30 ✓✓
35–36	48	42	36	30	24	18 ✓✓ ✓✓
37–38	1	2	4	8	16	32 ✓✓

B 7
10

Write these **improper fractions** as **mixed numbers** in their lowest terms.

39 $\frac{4}{3}$ = $\frac{2}{1}$ ✗

40 $\frac{5}{2}$ = $\frac{2}{1}$ ✗

41 $\frac{7}{3}$ = $\frac{3}{1}$ ✗

42 $\frac{6}{5}$ = $\frac{3}{1}$ ✗

43 $\frac{9}{2}$ = $\frac{6}{1}$ ✗

B 10
5

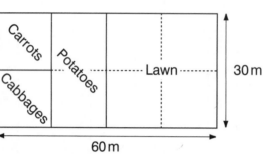

Carrots
Cabbages
Potatoes
Lawn
30 m
60 m

B12/B10
B 20

44 What percentage of the garden is lawn? 56% ✓

45 What fraction of the garden is for cabbages? 1. ✓

46 What percentage of the garden is for potatoes? ¼ % ✓

47 What fraction of the garden is for carrots? $\frac{1}{3}$ ✓

48 What is the area of the garden? 180 m² ✓

49 What is the area of the lawn? 45 m² ✗

50 What is three squared? 6 ✗

6
B 6
1

Now go to the Progress Chart to record your score! Total 50

Paper 2

Complete the following.

B3/B27
B 10

1 10 minutes × 10 = 1 hour

2 20p × ＿＿ = £1.00

3 50p × 4 = £2.00

4 $2\frac{1}{2}$ = ＿＿ halves

5 $1\frac{3}{4}$ = 13 quarters

6 10p × ＿＿ = £5.00

6

7 What is 5 squared? 25

8 What is 2^2? 4

9 Which number multiplied by itself gives 64? 8

10 The pairs of **factors** of 15 are: 1 and 15, 3 and 5 .

11–12 The pairs of **factors** of 12 are: 1 and 6 , 2 and 12 , 3 and 4.

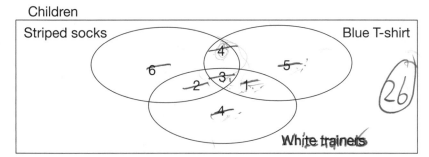

Children

Striped socks   Blue T-shirt

6   4   5

2   3   1

4

26

White trainers

Some children made this Venn diagram to show what they were wearing for PE.

13 How many children were there? 26

14 How many wore both blue T-shirts and white trainers? 4

15 How many wore blue T-shirts, white trainers and striped socks? 2

16 How many wore both white trainers and striped socks but not blue T-shirts? 1

17 How many wore either blue T-shirts or white trainers? 5

A library charges a fine of 40 pence for each week a book is late.

18 What is the fine if a book is 3 weeks late?

19 What is the fine if three books are 4 weeks late? 160

20 What is the fine if one book is 5 weeks late and two other books are 6 weeks late?

21 What are four sixes? 24

22 Find three lots of nine. 27

23 Seven times eight is 56

Underline the correct answer for each question.

24 $\frac{1}{2} + \frac{1}{4} =$ $\frac{3}{4}$ $\frac{1}{8}$ $\frac{3}{8}$ $\frac{1}{6}$

25 $1.00 - 0.9 =$ 0.01 1.9 1.1 0.1

26 $2 \div \frac{1}{2} =$ $\frac{1}{4}$ 1 4 2

27 How many $\frac{1}{2}$ in 2? $\frac{1}{4}$ 1 2 4

28 What is $\frac{1}{2}$ of 7? 14 $\frac{2}{7}$ $3\frac{1}{2}$ $6\frac{1}{2}$

40×4

B 6
3
B 5
3
B 2
B 14
5
B3/B2
3
B 3
3
B 10
B 11
5

29 What number when divided by 6 has an answer of 7 remainder 3? _45_

30 Divide 28 metres into 8 equal pieces. How long is each piece? _4_

31–36 Put a ring around the shapes which are regular **polygons**.

 A

 B

C

D

E

F

G

H

37 Which **polygon** is a **scalene triangle**? _H_

38 Which **polygon** has exactly 4 lines of symmetry? _B_

  39 Angle a = _90_

 40 Angle b = _120_

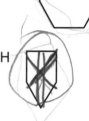 **41** Angle c = _6_

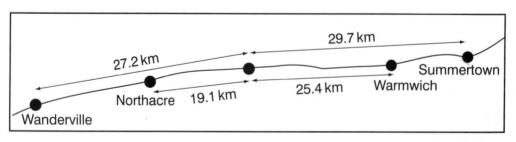

29.7 km

27.2 km

Northacre   19.1 km

25.4 km   Warmwich

Summertown

Wanderville

42 How far is it from Northacre to Summertown? _29.7_ km

43 How far is it from Wanderville to Summertown? _56.9_ km

44 How far is it from Warmwich to Northacre? _44.5_ km

45 How far is it from Warmwich to Wanderville? _06.4_ km

In a school of 300 children $\frac{3}{5}$ are boys.

46 How many boys are there?

47 How many girls are there?

Write the following fractions as decimals.

48 $\frac{1}{10}$ 10.0   49 $\frac{3}{100}$ 300   50 $\frac{17}{100}$ 1700

Now go to the Progress Chart to record your score!   Total   50

Paper 3

A train left Dover at 11:25 a.m. and arrived in London at 13:03.

1 How long did the journey take?   _____ h _____ min

Here are 6 numbers: 32   27   35   33   26   29

2 Find the largest and multiply it by the smallest.   _____

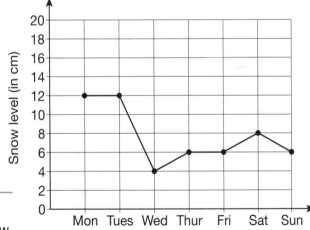

3 Underline the amounts below which you can make with these five coins.

19p   28p   33p   29p   37p

Here is a line graph that shows the amount of snow in one week.

4 Which day had the least amount of snow?

_____

5–6 On which days was the snow level higher than the day before?

_____ and _____

7–8 Mr Lee shovels his drive if there is more than 10 cm of snow. On which days did he shovel his drive? _____ and _____

9 Some offices close if there is more than 20 cm of snow. Did any offices close in this week?   _____

What number is halfway between:

10 20 and 30? _____   **11** 21 and 35? _____   **12** 17 and 29? _____

13 How many 250 g packets of biscuits can be made from 2 kg of biscuits? _____

Multiply each of these numbers by 10.

14 3.4 _____   **15** 14.6 _____   **16** 0.78 _____

17 2.68 _____   **18** 5.9 _____

Multiply each of these numbers by 100.

19 31.22 _____   **20** 0.56 _____   **21** 2.5 _____

22 0.27 _____   **23** 28 _____

CERTAIN   LIKELY   UNLIKELY   IMPOSSIBLE

Match one of these words to each of the statements below.

24 It will snow in Switzerland next year. _____

25 It will snow in the Sahara Desert next year. _____

26 A chocolate bar will grow wings and fly in Paris on Tuesday. _____

27 You will get some presents for your birthday. _____

Paul and Meena each have a piece of string. Paul's piece is 6.70 m long and Meena's is 5.84 m.

28 Who has the longer piece? _____

29 How many centimetres longer is it? _____

Here is a bar chart which shows the approximate number of people in Southwich who watch television each night.

Key
Watch BBC1
Watch ITV1

B 2
3
B25/B3
1
B 1
5
B 1
5
B 16
4
B 2
2
B14/B2

8

30–31 On which 2 nights do the same number of people watch BBC1 and ITV1?

_____ and _____

32 On which night is there the biggest difference in the number of people who watch BBC1 and ITV1? _____

33 BBC1 has the fewest viewers on _____

34 ITV1 has the fewest viewers on _____

35 How many more people watch ITV1 than BBC1 on Saturdays? _____

〔 6 〕

36 What number is the arrow pointing to below? _____

〔 B 6 〕

```
 ├──────┬──────┬──────┬──────┬──────┬──────┬──────┤
 −4     −3   ↑  −2    −1     0      1      2
```

〔 1 〕

〔 B 26 〕

37 Line A measures _____mm.   A   _____

38 Line B measures _____mm.   B   _____

39 Line C measures _____mm.   C   _____

40 Line D measures _____mm.   D   _____

〔 4 〕

If, on a map, 1 cm represents 1 km:

〔 B 25 〕

41 Line A would represent _____km.   **42** Line B would represent _____km.

43 Line C would represent _____km.   **44** Line D would represent _____km.

〔 4 〕

45 What is the biggest number you can make with these digits? 3, 6, 4, 8, 3, 2: _____

〔 B 1 〕

46 Write the answer to question 45 in words.

_____

〔 B 1 〕

47 If my car uses 1 litre of petrol every 10 km, how many litres will I need to go 105 km? _____

〔 B 3 〕

48 There are 3 boys for every 2 girls in a class of 25 children. How many girls are there? _____

〔 B 13 〕

〔 4 〕

〔 B 6 〕

49 Multiply 4 by itself. _____

50 What is 7^2? _____

〔 2 〕

Now go to the Progress Chart to record your score!   Total 〔 50 〕

Paper 4

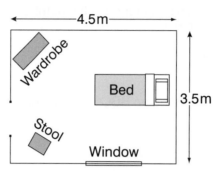

Scale: 1 cm represents 1 m

1–2 My bedroom is _____m long and is _____m wide.

3–4 The window is _____m long and the bed is _____m long.

5–6 The wardrobe is _____m long and the stool is _____m long.

B 26

6

7 How many times can I take 8 from 200?

8 Take the product of 6 and 7 from 50.

B3/B2

2

What is the best approximation for a mile? Underline your choice.

9 0.5 km   1 km   1.5 km   2 km   2.5 km

What is the best approximation for a gallon? Underline your choice.

10 1 litre   2 litres   3 litres   4 litres   5 litres   6 litres

B 25

B 25

2

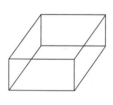

A

B

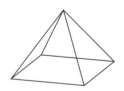

C

11–19 Complete the table.

B 21

	A	B	C
Number of **faces**			
Number of **vertices**			
Number of **edges**			

9

Write one of these signs $<$, $>$ or $=$ in the spaces below.

20 6×6 _____ $17 + 18$

21 3^2 _____ 2×5

22 $8 + 10 - 3$ _____ 5×3

23 $\frac{3}{4}$ hour _____ 50 seconds

24 0.5 m _____ 50 cm

25 $7 + 13$ _____ $6 + 7 + 8$

A 6
B3/B2
B6/B3
B2/B3
B 27
B 25
B 2
6

B 3
2

26 Share £37.50 equally between 25 boys. They would have £ _____ each.

27 Share £36.00 equally between 20 boys. They would have £ _____ each.

28 What fraction of the large square is covered with dots? _____

29 What fraction, in **lowest terms** is grey? _____

30 What fraction, in **lowest terms** is white? _____

31 What is the area of the whole large square? _____

32 What is the area of the grey squares? _____

33 What is the area of the white squares? _____

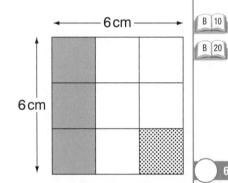

B 10
B 20
6

B 1

34 What is 7583 to the nearest 1000? _____

35–37 The distance from London to Jeddah is 5904 miles. This is approximately _____ miles to the nearest 1000 miles, _____ miles to the nearest 100 miles and _____ miles to the nearest 10 miles.

4

Use these two calculations to help you answer the following questions.

```
   712          357
 - 368        + 345
 ------       ------
   344          702
```

B 2

38 $368 + 344 =$ _____

39 $702 - 345 =$ _____

40 $712 - 368 =$ _____

41 $702 - 357 =$ _____

42 $712 - 344 =$ _____

5

43–46 Complete this multiplication table.

B 3

×				
	56	42	___	77
	___	48	32	88
	72	___	36	___

4

Write the answers to these fraction calculations in the **lowest terms**.

B 10

47 $\frac{2}{10} + \frac{7}{10} - \frac{1}{10} =$ _____

48 $\frac{9}{10} - \frac{6}{10} + \frac{2}{10} =$ _____

49 $\frac{9}{100} + \frac{90}{100} =$ _____

50 $\frac{24}{100} + \frac{13}{100} - \frac{8}{100} =$ _____

4

Now go to the Progress Chart to record your score! Total 50

Paper 5

B 1

1 What is 8536 to the nearest 1000? 9000

2 What is 8536 to the nearest 100? 8500

3 What is the biggest number you can make with these digits? 2 3 4 0 6 8

864,320

4 Write the answer to question 3 in words.

eight hundred thousand and sixty four · 3 hundred and 20

The distance from London to Sydney is 19 675 miles.

5–7 This is approximately _____ 000 miles to the nearest 1000 miles, _____ 100
miles to the nearest 100 miles and _____ miles to the nearest 10 miles.

40

7

8–12 Match the following by writing the most appropriate letter next to the time.

B 27

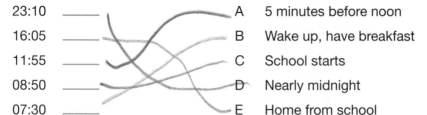

23:10	_____		A	5 minutes before noon
16:05	_____		B	Wake up, have breakfast
11:55	_____		C	School starts
08:50	_____		D	Nearly midnight
07:30	_____		E	Home from school

5

Write the next two numbers in each of the following lines.

B 7

13–14	15	20	30	45	65	70	80
15–16	$3\frac{1}{2}$	5	$6\frac{1}{2}$	8	$9\frac{1}{2}$	11	$12\frac{1}{2}$
17–18	1.85	1.90	1.95	2	2.05	2·10	2·15

19–20	2	4	7	11	16	*22* *26*
21–22	62	50	39	29	20	*16* *10*
23–24	1234	123.4	12.34	1.234	0.1234	*123* *12*

 12

25 What is 8 squared? *octagon*   **26** What is 11²? *2013*

 9 · 3

27 Which number multiplied by itself gives 81? *9*

B 5

Write in the missing numbers which complete the pairs of factors of:

28 14.   1 and 14, 2 and __*15*__ .

4

29–31 18.   1 and __*2*__ , __*2*__ and __*4*__ , 3 and 6.

32–34 Plot and label the points A (1, 0), B (2, 3), C (3, 0). Join up the points.

B 23

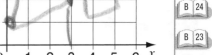

35 What is the name of this shape? *Heptagon*

B 18

36 How many lines of symmetry does it have? __*1*__

37 Translate the shape 2 units to the right. Draw the new position.

B 24

B 23

6

38 If the distance all round a square is 24 cm, what is the length of each side? __*10*__ cm

B 20

1

Look at the letters below. They form a pattern.

B 7

39 a b c d e a b c d e . . .   What would the 18th letter be? *c*

2

40 x y z x y z . . .   What would the 10th letter be? *x*

41 How many times can I take 28 from 756? *?*

B 3

1

42 478 + 199 = 677

B1/B2

If I took 100 away from both numbers (478 and 199) the answer would be:

the same   200 less   (100 more)

43 478 − 199 = 279

B1/B2

If I took 100 away from both numbers the answer would be:

the same   (200 less)   100 more

2

13

44 Add together $\frac{1}{8}$ and $\frac{1}{2}$.

45 How many quarters are there in $7\frac{3}{4}$?

In a school $\frac{3}{5}$ of the pupils were boys and there were 240 girls.

46 How many boys were in the school?

47 How many children were in the school?

48 How many days are there in the first 3 months of a leap year?

We have lessons from 9 o'clock till noon and then from 2 p.m. until 3:30 p.m.

We have two breaks of 15 minutes each in a day.

49–50 We work _____ hours a day and _____ hours a week.

B 10   2

B 10   2

B 27   1

B 27   2

Now go to the Progress Chart to record your score!   Total   50

Paper 6

Write the following decimals as **mixed numbers** in their **lowest terms**.   B 11

1 0.1 _____   **2** 0.03 _____   **3** 3.5 _____

4 2.1 _____   **5** 5.25 _____   **6** 9.75 _____

6

Underline the questions below which will have a remainder of 2.   B 3

7–8 64 ÷ 8   44 ÷ 6   100 ÷ 5   82 ÷ 10

9–10 38 ÷ 4   15 ÷ 5   74 ÷ 12   27 ÷ 4

4

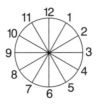

B 17

11 What size is the smaller angle between 12 and 3?   _____

12 What size is the smaller angle between 2 and 3?   _____

13 The smaller angle between 4 and 6 is   _____

14 The smaller angle between 6 and 9 is   _____

15 The angle between 6 and 12 is   _____

16 The smaller angle between 7 and 8 is   _____   6

17–20 Which numbers will come out of the machine?

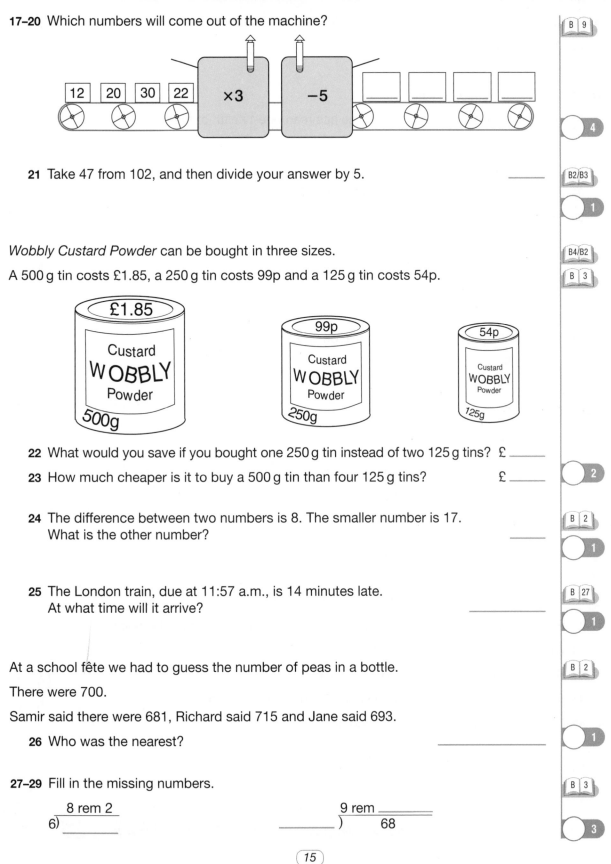

| 12 | 20 | 30 | 22 |

×3   −5

21 Take 47 from 102, and then divide your answer by 5. _____

Wobbly Custard Powder can be bought in three sizes.

A 500 g tin costs £1.85, a 250 g tin costs 99p and a 125 g tin costs 54p.

£1.85
Custard
WOBBLY
Powder
500g

99p
Custard
WOBBLY
Powder
250g

54p
Custard
WOBBLY
Powder
125g

22 What would you save if you bought one 250 g tin instead of two 125 g tins? £ _____

23 How much cheaper is it to buy a 500 g tin than four 125 g tins? £ _____

24 The difference between two numbers is 8. The smaller number is 17.
What is the other number? _____

25 The London train, due at 11:57 a.m., is 14 minutes late.
At what time will it arrive? _____

At a school fête we had to guess the number of peas in a bottle.

There were 700.

Samir said there were 681, Richard said 715 and Jane said 693.

26 Who was the nearest? _____

27–29 Fill in the missing numbers.

$$\begin{array}{r} 8 \text{ rem } 2 \\ 6\overline{)} \end{array}$$

$$\begin{array}{r} 9 \text{ rem } \rule{2cm}{0.4pt} \\ \rule{2cm}{0.4pt}\overline{)\ 68} \end{array}$$

B 9

4

B2/B3

1

B4/B2

B 3

2

B 2

1

B 27

1

B 2

1

B 3

3

15

School starts at 8:55 a.m. One day Katie was a quarter of an hour late.

30 What time did she arrive? _____

B 27
1

There are 720 books in the school library.

31 How many books has John read if he has read one-twelfth of them? _____

B 10
1

The sum of the ages of Will and Annette is 20.

32 If Will is 4 years older than Annette, how old is he? _____

33 How old is Annette? _____

B3/B2
2

34 Multiply 47 by 200. _____

B 3
1

Put a sign in each space so that each question will be correct.

35–36 (5 _____ 9) _____ 8 = 6

37–38 (12 _____ 4) _____ 3 = 6

39–40 (6 _____ 3) _____ 4 = 36

B2/B3
6

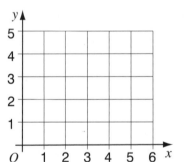

41–44 Plot and label the points A (2, 5), B (1, 5), C (1, 1), D (2, 1). Join up the points.

45 What is the name of this shape? _____

46 How many lines of symmetry does it have? _____

47 Translate the shape 3 units to the right. Draw the new position.

48–49 Draw all the diagonals in the second shape.

B 23
B 19
B 24
B 23
9

50 What number is 12 more than 19? _____

B 2
1

Paper 7

Some children were asked which instruments they played. They made this Venn diagram.

B 2
B 14

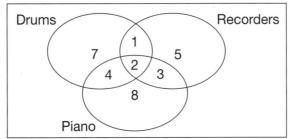

1 How many children were asked? _____

2 How many play the drums? _____

3 How many children play both the piano and the drums? _____

4 How many children play both the recorder and the drums but not the piano? _____

5 How many children play the piano, the recorder and the drums? _____

5

Fill in the missing numbers.

B 8

6 $7 \times (\clubsuit + 2) = 56$ $\clubsuit = $ _____

7 $12 \div (\heartsuit - 2) = 3$ $\heartsuit = $ _____

8 $7 + 5 \times \spadesuit = 36$ $\spadesuit = $ _____

9 $(7 - 5) \times \blacklozenge + 3 = 7$ $\blacklozenge = $ _____

4

10 Add half of 8 to twice 6. _____

B2/B3
1

B 20

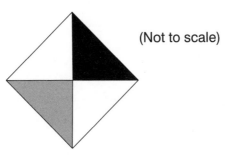

(Not to scale)

11 What is the area of this square? Each side is 4 cm. _____

12 What is the area of the grey part? _____

13 What is the total area of the white parts? _____

3

At Ladybird School there are 30 children in each of the 4 classes.

Here is a bar chart to show the children who can swim.

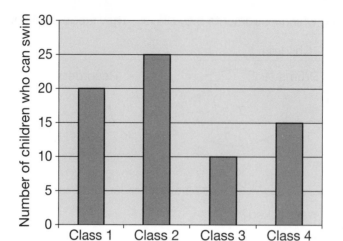

14–21 Complete this frequency table.

Class	Number who *can* swim	Number who *cannot* swim
1		
2		
3		
4		

22 What fraction of the whole school, in **lowest terms** can swim? _____

23 What fraction of the whole school, in **lowest terms** cannot swim? _____

24 In which class can 50% of the children swim? _____

25 In which class can $\frac{2}{3}$ of the children swim? _____

26 In which class is the ratio of children who can swim to those who cannot swim 1:2? _____

Write how many halves there are in:

27 $7\frac{1}{2}$ _____   **28** $10\frac{1}{2}$ _____   **29** 23 _____

30 How many times can I subtract 0.05 from 5? _____

31–33 There are 96 roses in a bed in the park. 50% of them are yellow, $\frac{1}{4}$ are red, and the rest are pink.

_____ roses are red, _____ are yellow and _____ are pink.

(18)

Write the number of pairs of parallel sides in each **polygon**.

B 19

34 [square] _____

35 [trapezoid] _____

36 [octagon] _____

37 [pentagon] _____

4

Petrol costs 137p a litre at garage A, 139p a litre at garage B and 138p a litre at garage C. Carol has £27.50 and she needs to fill up her tank with 20 litres of petrol.

B3/B2

38 20 litres cost £ _____ at garage A.   **39** 20 litres cost £ _____ at garage B.

40 20 litres cost £ _____ at garage C.

41 Which garage should Carol go to, to fill up her car?   _____

42 How much more money would she need if she went to the most expensive garage?   £ _____

5

My watch gains 2 minutes in every 24 hours.

B 27

43 If I put it right at 10 a.m. on Monday, what time will it show at 10 p.m. the same night?   _____ p.m.

44 What time will it show at 10 a.m. on Tuesday?   _____ a.m.

45 What time will it show at 10 a.m. on Wednesday?   _____ a.m.

46 What time will it show at 10 a.m. on the following Monday?   _____ a.m.

4

Jasmina and Sharon shared 24 book tokens.

B2/B3

47–48 Jasmina had 2 more than Sharon, so she had _____ and Sharon had _____.

2

B 27

49 How many minutes are there between noon and 13:29?   _____

50 How many weeks are there in 266 days?   _____

2

Now go to the Progress Chart to record your score!   Total   50

Paper 8

1 How many US dollars do you get for £100? $ _____

2 How many Sri Lankan rupees do you get for £50?   _____ rupees

3 How many euros do you get for £30?   € _____

4 How many pounds do you get for 380 Sri Lankan rupees?   £ _____

B3/B13

| £1 = 1.65 US dollars |
| £1 = 1.2 euros |
| £1 = 190 Sri Lankan rupees |

4

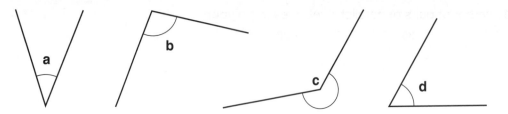

Using the words **acute**, **obtuse** or **reflex** describe the above angles. Use a protractor to find the size of the angles to the nearest 1°.

5–6 **a** is _____ , and is approximately _____°.

7–8 **b** is _____ , and is approximately _____°.

9–10 **c** is _____ , and is approximately _____°.

11–12 **d** is _____ , and is approximately _____°.

Here is a bar chart showing the temperatures in seven cities last winter.

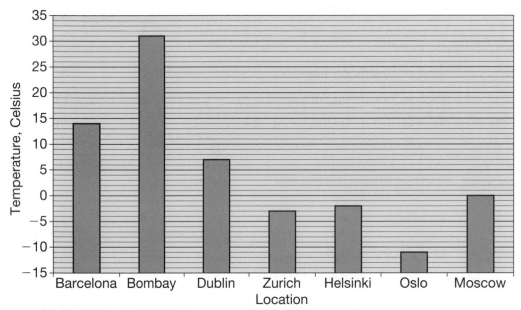

Find the difference in temperature between:

13 Bombay and Dublin.   _____ °C

14 Zurich and Barcelona.   _____ °C

15 Moscow and Zurich.   _____ °C

16 Helsinki and Oslo.   _____ °C

What is the remainder when:

17 25 is divided by 7?   _____

18 46 is divided by 11?   _____

19 67 is divided by 4?   _____

20 7.49	21 1.78	22 1.68
+ 8.56	+ 2.56	+ 2.37
———	———	———

Here are the dates of birth of six children.

A 30/12/08	B 7/8/07	C 29/10/07
D 24/12/07	E 20/5/08	F 29/2/08

23 Who is the oldest?   ———

24 Who is the youngest?   ———

25 Who has a birthday during the summer holidays?   ———

26 Who has a birthday only 'once every 4 years'?   ———

27 Whose birthday is in October?   ———

In 4 years' time Wilf will be half as old as his dad. Wilf's dad is 33 next year.

28 How old is Wilf now?   ———

If Emma were 3 cm taller she would be twice the height of her brother. He is 75 cm tall.

29 How tall is Emma?   ——— m

The pie chart shows the favourite sports of 32 children.

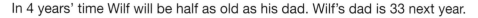

30 How many children prefer football?   ———

31 How many children prefer cricket?   ———

32 How many children prefer swimming?   ———

33 Which sport is as popular as swimming?   —————

34 What percentage of the class prefer cricket?   ———%

35 What fraction of the class prefer cycling?   ———

Find the answers to these calculations.

36 1997 + 455 =   ———

37 3003 − 996 =   ———

38 4577 − 994 =   ———

39–43 Put a decimal point in each of the following numbers so that the 3 has a value of $\frac{3}{10}$.

B1/B10

$$1\ 2\ 3\ 4 \qquad 1\ 4\ 2\ 3 \qquad 1\ 3\ 2\ 4 \qquad 1\ 2\ 4\ 3 \qquad 4\ 3\ 2\ 1$$

Write the correct sign in each space ($<$, $>$ or $=$).

44 $4 + 7 - 1$ _____ 2×5

45 5×9 _____ $9 + 5$

46 $30 \div 6$ _____ 3×2

47 $\frac{1}{2}$ hour _____ 4×7 min

48 3 litres _____ 2000 ml

49 150 cm _____ 2 m

50 What is the perimeter of a room which is 3.2 m long and 2.5 m wide? _____ m

Now go to the Progress Chart to record your score! **Total** ( ) 50

Paper 9

Look at the patterns below.

1 1a2b3c1a2b3c … . What would the 20th symbol be? _____

9g8f7e6d9g8f … . What would the:

2 23rd symbol be? _____

3 40th symbol be? _____

There are 240 books in our library. 10% are about sport, $\frac{1}{8}$ are about nature, $\frac{1}{6}$ are about travel, 20% are adventure stories and $\frac{1}{3}$ are school stories.

4–5 _____ books are about travel and _____ are school stories.

6–7 _____ books are about nature and _____ are adventure stories.

8 How many books about sport are there? _____

9 How many other books are in the library? _____

10 Take forty-nine from two thousand and ten. _____

11 What is the area of this carpet in m²? _____

12 How many tiles of size 50 cm × 50 cm will fit in a square size 1 m × 1 m? _____

13 How many times can you put 2500 cm² into 15 m²? _____

3 m

5 m

1 m

Floor tiles   1 m

Here are some thermometers which show the temperatures at midday each day for one week last winter.

C
10°
9°
8°
7°
6°
5°
4°
3°
2°
1°
0°

Mon Tues Wed Thur Fri Sat Sun

14–16 On which days was the temperature lower than the day before?

_____ and _____ and _____

17–19 On which days was the temperature higher than the previous day?

_____ and _____ and _____

20 Which day had the lowest temperature? _____

21 Which day had the highest temperature? _____

22–23 Between which consecutive days was the biggest difference in temperature?

_____ and _____

24 Find the **range** in temperature during the week. _____

25 Which temperature was the **mode**? _____

12

26 How many days are there in spring (March, April and May)? _____

27 Find the length of a queue of 21 cars (each car is 4 m long).

There is a space of 1 m between each pair of cars. _____

2

2cm 2cm 2cm

A   B

C   D

28 Into how many squares the size of A could the large square be divided? _____

29–31 Find the area of:

square A _____

the large square _____

the cross _____

32 What is the perimeter of the large square? _____

5

23

33 $2000 - 2 =$ _____ **34** $350 + 63 =$ _____ **35** $1990 + 20 =$ _____

B 2

3

At a youth club there are 3 boys for every 4 girls.

B 13

B 2

36 If there are 12 boys at the club, how many girls are there? _____

At another youth club there are also 3 boys for every 4 girls.

37 If there are 12 girls at the club, how many boys are there? _____

38 How many children altogether go to both youth clubs? _____

3

B 17

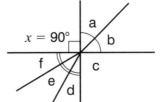

Angle a = Angle b

Angle d = Angle e = Angle f

39 Angle a = _____   **40** Angle c = _____   **41** Angle e = _____

42 Angle a + b + c + d + e + f + x = _____

4

| 51 | 67 | 80 | 91 | 143 |

B 3

B 5

Which of the numbers in the box:

43 is divisible by 7? _____   **44** is divisible by 3? _____

45 is divisible by 11? _____

3

The product of 2 numbers is 42. One of the numbers is 7.

B 3

46 What is the other number? _____

The distance all around a room is 24 m. The room is twice as long as it is wide.

B 20

47 Its length is _____m.   **48** Its width is _____m.

3

B 1

49 What is the smallest number you can make with these digits? 3, 5, 4, 9, 3, 4

_____

50 Write the answer to question 49 in words.

_____

2

Paper 10

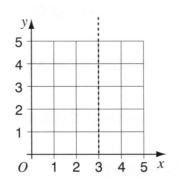

1–4 Plot and label the points A (4, 1), B (3, 4), C (4, 5), D (5, 4). Join up the points.

5 Reflect the shape in the mirror line. Draw all the diagonals in the second shape.

6 How many lines of symmetry does the whole shape have? _____

Put a sign in each space so that each question will be correct.

7–8 (5 _____ 2) _____ 4 = 3

9–10 (8 _____ 1) _____ 2 = 9

11–12 (8 _____ 3) _____ 2 = 10

13–14 (3 _____ 6) _____ 4 = 5

Arrange the following numbers in order, starting with the smallest.

15–19   2.111   2.1   2.01   2.11   2.101

_____   _____   _____   _____   _____

20–22 Show that 456 multiplied by 30 is 13 680 using the following grid.

×	400	50	6
30			

23 How many glasses, each holding $\frac{1}{4}$ litre, could be filled from a bottle holding 2.5 litres? _____

24 What is the smallest number which must be added to 368 to make it exactly divisible by 27? _____

25 How many squares 5 cm × 5 cm can I cut from a card 20 cm × 40 cm? _____

26 How much do I have left from £3.00 after buying 4 flowers at 65p each? _____ p

27 I went to the cinema at 2:55 p.m. and came out at 5:35 p.m. How long was I there? _____ h _____ min

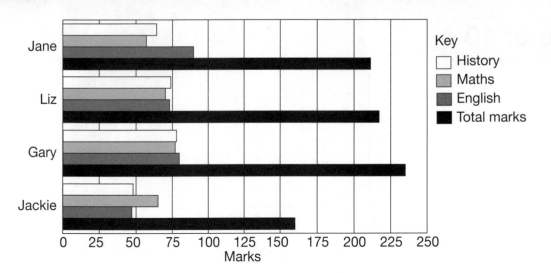

28 _____ had the highest marks in any exam.

29 The highest total mark was achieved by _____.

30 Who gained fewer than 50 marks in two exams? _____

31 _____ gained over 75 marks in three exams.

32 Who was second in Maths? _____

A	B	C	D	E
$P = n - 4$	$n = 4 - P$	$P = n + 4$	$P = 4n$	$P = \dfrac{n}{4}$

Match each of these equations to one of the following statements.

33 In a café, four people are sitting at each table. There are P people and n tables. _____

34 The period of time, P, is 4 days longer than the numbers of days worked, n. _____

35 n is the total prize money shared between four people. P is the amount that each will receive. _____

36 n is the change left from £4 when P is spent buying a bag of potatoes. _____

37 The number of members of a club present at a meeting, P, is 4 less than the total number of members in the club, n. _____

I went to bed at 7:30 p.m. and got up at 7:15 a.m. the next day.

38 How long was I in bed? _____ h _____ min

There are 28 in our class. One day there were 6 times as many present as there were absent.

39 How many were present? _____

40 How many were absent? _____

Write in quarters:

41–44 $2\frac{1}{4}$ = _____ $1\frac{3}{4}$ = _____ $2\frac{3}{4}$ = _____ $1\frac{1}{4}$ = _____

45–48 3 = _____ $4\frac{1}{4}$ = _____ $3\frac{3}{4}$ = _____ $4\frac{3}{4}$ = _____

49 Kim has 75p and Michael has 91p. How much must Michael give Kim so that they will both have the same amount?   _____

50 How much will each of them have then?   _____

Now go to the Progress Chart to record your score!   **Total**   **50**

Paper 11

1 What is $6^2 - 3^2$?   _____

Shop A had 1 litre of apple juice for £1.80, shop B had 250 ml for 55p, shop C had $\frac{3}{4}$ litre for £1.47 and shop D had 500 ml for £1.05.

2 Shop _____ was the cheapest.   **3** Shop _____ was 2nd cheapest.

4 Shop _____ was 3rd cheapest.   **5** Shop _____ was the dearest.

   A   B   C   D

6 A contains _____ml.   **7** B contains _____ml.

8 C contains _____ml.   **9** D contains _____ml.

10–13 How much would I have to add to each jug to fill it up to 1 litre?

   A _____ml   B _____ml   C _____ml   D _____ml

Fill in the missing numbers.

14 $\dfrac{7 \text{ rem } 3}{8)\qquad}$

15 $\dfrac{5 \text{ rem } 4}{9)\qquad}$

16 $\dfrac{\rule{2cm}{0.4pt} \text{ rem } 3}{7)\quad 38}$

17 $\dfrac{\rule{2cm}{0.4pt} \text{ rem } 3}{9)\quad 39}$

18–21 Write down all the numbers between 30 and 60 which are multiples of 8.

_____   _____   _____   _____

B 5
4

22–24 Write down all the numbers between 30 and 50 which are exactly divisible by 7.

_____   _____   _____

B5/B3
3

25–28 Put a decimal point in each of the following numbers so that the 7 will have the value of 7 units.

8 9 7 5 6   5 7 9 5 6   7 9 8 5 6   9 8 6 7 5

B 1
4

29–34 The distance from London to New York is 6799 miles. This is approximately _____ miles to the nearest 1000 miles, _____ miles to the nearest 100 miles and _____ miles to the nearest 10 miles.

The distance from London to Madras is 9981 miles. This is approximately _____ miles to the nearest 1000 miles, _____ miles to the nearest 100 miles and _____ miles to the nearest 10 miles.

B 1
6

Diesel costs 85.9p a litre at petrol station A, 84.9p a litre at petrol station B and 86.9p a litre at petrol station C. Doug needs 30 litres to top up the fuel tank in his van.

35–37 What would 30 litres of diesel cost at each petrol station?

A £ _____   B £ _____   C £ _____

B3/B2

When he stopped for fuel, Doug also bought a road atlas for £3.96 and a cup of coffee for £1.98. His total bill was £32.01.

38 Which petrol station did he stop at?   _____

39 How much would he have saved on fuel, if he had gone to the cheapest petrol station instead?   £ _____

5

Write the next two numbers in each of the following lines.

40–41   8   4   2   1   _____   _____

42–43   1.25   1.50   1.75   _____   _____

B 7
4

Which of the numbers in the triangle:

44 has a remainder of 3 when divided by 7?   _____

45 has a remainder of 4 when divided by 8?   _____

46 can be divided exactly by 5 and 6?   _____

B 3
B 5

55
47   19
24
30   68

47 has a remainder of 3 when divided by 8? _____

48 has a remainder of 2 when divided by 5? _____

There are 24 in our class. $\frac{3}{8}$ of the children are girls.

49–50 There are _____ girls and _____ boys in the class.

Now go to the Progress Chart to record your score!   Total   50

Paper 12

240 children are going out for the day by bus. Each bus can carry 52 children.

1 How many buses are needed? _____

A train departs at 07:49 and arrives at 10:13.

2 How long is the journey? _____ h _____ min

Multiply each of these numbers by 100.

3 0.24 _____   **4** 0.0076 _____   **5** 0.75 _____

Here is a plan of our bathroom.
Scale: 2 cm = 1 m

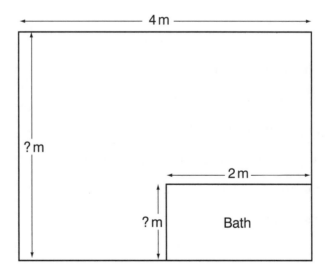

6 What is the perimeter of the bathroom? _____

7 We would need _____ floor tiles of 50 cm × 50 cm to cover the whole floor.

8 We decide not to put the tiles under the bath.
How many do we now need? _____

9 What is the area of the bath? _____

10 What is the area of the bathroom? _____

There are 30 children in Class 4. There are 2 girls to every 3 boys.

11–12 There are _____ girls and _____ boys in Class 4.

2

13–16 The pairs of **factors** of 28 are: 1 and 28, _____ and _____ , _____ and _____

17–26 The pairs of **factors** of 36 are: _____ and _____ , _____ and _____ ,

_____ and _____ , _____ and _____ , _____ and _____

14

The children in our class made a Venn diagram to show how many had dark hair and brown eyes.

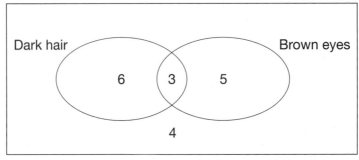

Our class

27 How many children are in our class? _____

28 How many children have dark hair? _____

29 How many have brown eyes? _____

30 How many have both dark hair and brown eyes? _____

31 _____ children don't have dark hair.

32 _____ children don't have brown eyes.

6

Fill in the missing numbers.

B 3
B 11

33 $5 \times 6 \times$ _____ $= 300$

34 $3 \times 4 \times$ _____ $= 240$

35 $7 \times 2 \times$ _____ $= 56$

36 $8 \times 3 \times$ _____ $= 96$

37 $5 \times 8 \times$ _____ $= 200$

38 $10 \times 3 \times$ _____ $= 270$

39 $3 \times 0.007 =$ _____

40 $4 \times 1.01 =$ _____

8

Any answer that requires units of measurement should be marked wrong if the correct units have not been included.

Paper 1

1 $\frac{1}{2}$
2 $\frac{3}{5}$
3 $\frac{1}{2}$
4 $\frac{2}{3}$
5 $\frac{1}{2}$
6 $\frac{1}{4}$
7 $\frac{1}{2}$
8 $\frac{18}{35}$
9 $\times$
10 $-$
11 $\times$
12 $+$
13 14
14 8
15 31

16–20

21 32
22 Green
23 Yellow
24–25 Red, Pink
26 16
27 16
28 1
29 50
30 25
31 21
32 24
33 35
34 30
35 24
36 18
37 16
38 32
39 $1\frac{1}{3}$
40 $2\frac{1}{2}$
41 $2\frac{1}{3}$
42 $1\frac{1}{5}$
43 $4\frac{1}{2}$
44 50
45 $\frac{1}{8}$
46 25
47 $\frac{1}{8}$
48 1800
49 900
50 9

Paper 2

1 6
2 5
3 4
4 5
5 7
6 50
7 25
8 4
9 8
10 5
11 12
12 6
13 25
14 4
15 3
16 2
17 19
18 £1.20
19 £4.80
20 £6.80
21 24
22 27
23 56
24 $\frac{3}{4}$
25 0.1
26 4
27 4
28 $3\frac{1}{2}$
29 45
30 3.5 m or $3\frac{1}{2}$ m
31–36 A, B, C, D, F, G
37 E
38 F
39 55°
40 30°
41 60°
42 48.8
43 56.9
44 44.5
45 52.6
46 180
47 120
48 0.1
49 0.03
50 0.17

Paper 3

1 1 h 38 min
2 910
3 28p, 33p, 37p
4 Wednesday or Wed
5–6 Thursday, Saturday or Thur, Sat
7–8 Monday, Tuesday or Mon, Tues
9 No
10 25
11 28
12 23
13 8
14 34
15 146
16 7.8
17 26.8
18 59
19 3122
20 56
21 250
22 27
23 2800
24 Certain or Likely
25 Unlikely or Impossible
26 Impossible
27 Likely or Certain
28 Paul
29 86 cm
30–31 Wednesday, Sunday
32 Friday
33 Monday
34 Tuesday
35 500
36 −2.5
37 40
38 55
39 50
40 25
41 4
42 5.5
43 5
44 2.5
45 864 332
46 eight hundred and sixty-four thousand three hundred and thirty-two
47 10.5 or $10\frac{1}{2}$ litres
48 10
49 16
50 49

Paper 4

1 4.5 or $4\frac{1}{2}$
2 3.5 or $3\frac{1}{2}$
3 1.5 or $1\frac{1}{2}$
4 2
5 1
6 0.5 or $\frac{1}{2}$
7 25
8 8
9 1.5 km
10 4 litres or 5 litres

Bond Maths Assessment Papers 9–10 years Book 1

ANSWERS

11–19

	A	B	C
Number of faces	6	5	5
Number of vertices	8	6	5
Number of edges	12	9	8

20 >
21 <
22 =
23 >
24 =
25 <
26 1.50
27 1.80
28 $\frac{1}{9}$
29 $\frac{1}{3}$
30 $\frac{5}{9}$
31 36 cm²
32 12 cm²
33 20 cm²
34 8000
35 6000
36 5900
37 5900
38 712
39 357
40 344
41 345
42 368

43–46

×	(8)	(6)	(4)	(11)
(7)	56	42	**28**	77
(8)	**64**	48	32	88
(9)	72	**54**	36	**99**

47 $\frac{4}{5}$
48 $\frac{1}{2}$
49 $\frac{99}{100}$
50 $\frac{29}{100}$

Paper 5

1 9000
2 8500
3 864 320
4 eight hundred and sixty-four thousand three hundred and twenty
5 20 000
6 19 700
7 19 680
8 D
9 E
10 A
11 C

12 B
13 90
14 120
15 11
16 $12\frac{1}{2}$
17 2.1 or 2.10
18 2.15
19 22
20 29
21 12
22 5
23 0.01234
24 0.001234
25 64
26 121
27 9
28 7
29 18
30 2
31 9

32–34

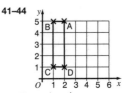

35 isosceles triangle
36 1
37

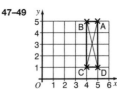

38 6
39 c
40 x
41 27
42 200 less
43 the same
44 $\frac{5}{8}$
45 31
46 360
47 600
48 91
49 4
50 20

Paper 6

1 $\frac{1}{10}$
2 $\frac{3}{100}$
3 $3\frac{1}{2}$
4 $2\frac{1}{10}$
5 $5\frac{1}{4}$
6 $9\frac{3}{4}$
7–8 44 ÷ 6, 82 ÷ 10
9–10 38 ÷ 4, 74 ÷ 12

11 90°
12 30°
13 60°
14 90°
15 180°
16 30°
17 31
18 55
19 85
20 61
21 11
22 0.09
23 0.31
24 25
25 12:11 p.m.
26 Jane
27 $\begin{array}{r} 8 \text{ rem } 2 \\ 6)\ \mathbf{50} \end{array}$
28–29 $\begin{array}{r} 9 \text{ rem } \mathbf{5} \\ 7)\ 68 \end{array}$
30 9:10 a.m.
31 60
32 12
33 8
34 9400
35–36 (5 + 9) − 6
37–38 (12 ÷ 4) + 3
39–40 (6 + 3) × 4
41–44

45 rectangle
46 2

47–49

50 31

Paper 7

1 30
2 14
3 6
4 1
5 2
6 6
7 6
8 3
9 2
10 16

11 16 cm²
12 4 cm²
13 8 cm²

14–21

Class	No. who *can* swim	No. who *cannot* swim
1	**20**	**10**
2	**25**	**5**
3	**10**	**20**
4	15	15

22 $\frac{7}{12}$
23 $\frac{5}{12}$
24 Class 4
25 Class 1
26 Class 3
27 15
28 21
29 46
30 100
31 24
32 48
33 24
34 2
35 1
36 4
37 0
38 27.40
39 27.80
40 27.60
41 A
42 0.30
43 10:01
44 10:02
45 10:04
46 10:14
47 13
48 11
49 89
50 38

Paper 8

1 165
2 9500
3 36
4 2
5 acute
6 40
7 obtuse
8 100
9 reflex
10 230
11 acute
12 60
13 24
14 17
15 3

16 9
17 4
18 2
19 3
20 16.05
21 4.34
22 4.05
23 B
24 A
25 B
26 F
27 C
28 14
29 1.47
30 8
31 16
32 4
33 cycling
34 50
35 $\frac{1}{8}$
36 2452
37 2007
38 3583
39 12.34
40 142.3
41 1.324
42 124.3
43 4.321
44 =
45 >
46 <
47 >
48 >
49 <
50 11.4

Paper 9

1 a
2 6
3 d
4 40
5 80
6 30
7 48
8 24
9 18
10 1961
11 15 m²
12 4
13 60
14–16 Tues, Wed, Fri
17–19 Thurs, Sat, Sun
20 Fri
21 Mon
22–23 Thurs, Fri
24 7°C (8 − 1)
25 4°C
26 92
27 104 m
28 9

29 4 cm²
30 36 cm²
31 20 cm²
32 24 cm
33 1998
34 413
35 2010
36 16
37 9
38 49
39 45°
40 90°
41 30°
42 360°
43 91
44 51
45 143
46 6
47 8
48 4
49 334 459
50 three hundred and thirty-four thousand four hundred and fifty-nine

Paper 10

1–5

6 1
7 +
8 −
9 −
10 +
11 −
12 ×
13 +
14 −
15 2.01
16 2.1
17 2.101
18 2.11
19 2.111

20–22

×	400	50	6
30	**12 000**	**1500**	**180**

23 10
24 10
25 32
26 40p
27 2 h 40 min
28 Jane
29 Gary
30 Jackie
31 Gary

ANSWERS

Bond Maths Assessment Papers 9–10 years Book 1

32 Liz
33 D
34 C
35 E
36 B
37 A
38 11 h 45 min
39 24
40 4
41 $\frac{9}{4}$
42 $\frac{7}{4}$
43 $\frac{11}{4}$
44 $\frac{5}{4}$
45 $\frac{12}{4}$
46 $\frac{17}{4}$
47 $\frac{15}{4}$
48 $\frac{19}{4}$
49 8p
50 83p

Paper 11

1 27
2 A
3 C
4 D
5 B
6 900 ml
7 700 ml
8 300 ml
9 500 ml
10 100 ml
11 300 ml
12 700 ml
13 500 ml
14 59
15 49
16 5
17 4
18–21 32, 40, 48, 56
22–24 35, 42, 49
25 897.56
26 57.956
27 7.9856
28 9867.5
29 7000
30 6800
31 6800
32 10 000
33 10 000
34 9980
35 25.77
36 25.47
37 26.07
38 C
39 0.60
40 0.5 or $\frac{1}{2}$
41 0.25 or $\frac{1}{4}$
42 2
43 2.25

44 24
45 68
46 30
47 19
48 47
49 9
50 15

Paper 12

1 5
2 2 h 24 min
3 24
4 0.76
5 75
6 14 m
7 48
8 40
9 2 m^2
10 12 m^2
11 12
12 18
13–16 2 and 14, 4 and 7
17–26 1 and 36, 2 and 18, 3 and 13, 4 and 9, 6 and 6
27 18
28 9
29 8
30 3
31 9
32 10
33 10
34 20
35 4
36 4
37 5
38 9
39 0.021
40 4.04
41 50%
42 20%
43 100%
44 80%
45 25%
46 60%
47 267
48 437
49 377
50 507

Paper 13

1–4

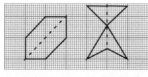

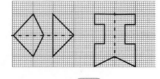

5 16
6 9
7 5
8 2
9 3
10 $\frac{1}{3}$ or $\frac{9}{27}$
11 9 km^2
12 12 km
13 4 km
14 16 km
15 374
16 474
17 674
18–21 A, C, F, G
22 12
23 5
24 8
25 20
26 90°
27 180°
28 135°
29 5
30 9
31 6
32 5
33 9
34 3
35 11:57 a.m.
36 400
37 13
38 23
39 54
40 105 m
41 150 m
42 105 m
43 30 m
44 120 m
45 60 m
46 135 m
47 90 m
48 17
49 294
50 4

Paper 14

1 TRUE
2 FALSE
3 FALSE
4 FALSE
5–8
9 quadrilateral
10 trapezium
11

12 1
13 3 litres
14 26 cm
15 $1\frac{1}{10}$
16 $2\frac{6}{7}$
17 5
18 8
19 7
20 11
21 6
22 15
23 0.23
24 0.17
25 0.3
26 0.09
27 216 824
28 216 486
29 21 648.6
30 21 484
31 21 426
32 52
33 10 014
34 27
35 85 cm
36 20:55
37 22:10
38 17
39 9
40 1
41 8
42 13
43 5
44 26
45
    (children) 4
    4
46 5
47 $\frac{7}{30}$
48 $\frac{1}{30}$
49 35
50 12

Paper 15

1 $1\frac{3}{10}$
2 $1\frac{2}{5}$
3 $2\frac{2}{3}$
4 TRUE
5 FALSE
6 TRUE
7 TRUE
8 FALSE
9 80
10 1
11 2000
12 200
13 8000
14 5000
15 8

16 1 cm
17 4 cm
18 5 cm
19 4.5 cm or $4\frac{1}{2}$ cm
20 3.5 cm or $3\frac{1}{2}$ cm
21 2.5 cm or $2\frac{1}{2}$ cm
22 56
23 7474
24 44 660
25 93.04
26 $\frac{10}{3}$
27 $\frac{9}{2}$
28 $\frac{7}{4}$
29 $\frac{7}{6}$
30 $\frac{11}{5}$
31 $\frac{14}{3}$
32 <
33 >
34 600 m²
35 $\frac{1}{3}$
36 $\frac{1}{6}$
37 100 m²
38 100 m
39 12 356
40 12 365
41 65 321
42 65 312
43–44

45 70%
46 20%
47 50%
48 25%
49 40%
50 80%

Paper 16

1 110
2 121
3 4
4 $4\frac{1}{4}$
5 0.987
6 0.0987
7 16.19
8 1.36
9 49.36
10 3.49
11 100
12 90
13 Wednesday

14 630
15 <
16 >
17 8.75 m²
18 3.5 m
19 7061
20 2
21 6
22 2
23 4
24 6 m
25 3 m
26 0.0355
27 0.0305
28 0.305
29 3.035
30 30.5
31 0.8
32 77
33 50
34 16
35 5 h 42 min
36 310
37 312
38 263
39 318
40 Min
41 Steven
42 Jerzy
43 14
44 Min
45 81
46 121
47 45
48 600
49 400
50 1000

Paper 17

1 12.9 km
2 12 km
3 13.8 km
4 12.9 km
5 21 ÷ 6
6 19 ÷ 4
7 24 ÷ 7
8 27 ÷ 8
9 6th or sixth
10 68
11 7
12–13 Music and sci-fi
14 $\frac{1}{15}$
15–16 Sport, Nature
17 10%
18 20%
19 £6.90
20 $7\frac{1}{2}$ kg or 7.5 kg
21 456
22 £2.60
23 74

Bond Maths Assessment Papers 9–10 years Book 1

24 466
25 843
26 567
27 801
28 9823
29 25
30 27
31 93
32 45.6
33 16.4 m
34 3.6 m

35–45

46 07:30
47 10:45
48 22:15
49 35p or £0.35
50 103 500

Paper 18

1 $\frac{2}{5}$
2 $\frac{1}{4}$
3 $\frac{9}{10}$
4 $\frac{3}{100}$
5 $\frac{1}{100}$
6 $\frac{7}{100}$
7 7 cm²
8 9 cm²
9 9 cm²
10 20
11 157
12 85
13 208
14–17 1 and 27, 3 and 9
18–23 1 and 16, 2 and 8, 4 and 4
24 20
25 10
26 5
27 42
28 61
29 48
30 71
31 306
32 605
33 100
34 20
35 1.560 or 1.56
36 17.72
37 58.86
38 16.25 or 16.250
39 (9 × 12) ———— (4 × 50)
   (11 × 11) ———— (9 × 11)
   (20 × 10) ———— (120 + 1)
   (102 − 3) ———— (110 − 2)

40 acute
41 obtuse
42 right angle
43 obtuse
44 22
45 12
46 7
47 4
48 10
49 15
50 35p

Paper 19

1 2
2 44
3 42
4 2
5 5
6 48
7–8 8, 9
9 1228
10 2 cm
11 3.5 cm or $3\frac{1}{2}$ cm
12 2.5 cm or $2\frac{1}{2}$ cm
13 2.5 cm or $2\frac{1}{2}$ cm
14 12
15 21
16 2
17 3
18 25
19 500
20 1000
21 3.46
22 122
23 2500
24 FALSE
25 FALSE

26–34

	A	B	C
Number of faces	6	7	10
Number of vertices	8	10	16
Number of edges	12	15	24

35 8
36 14
37 9
38 7
39 $\frac{1}{4}$
40 0.01
41 16
42 1.9
43 1.11
44 33
45 90 m
46 08:35 or 8:35 a.m.
47 42
48 6
49 80
50 120

Paper 20

1 $\frac{5}{16}$
2 $\frac{3}{16}$
3 $\frac{7}{16}$
4 $\frac{1}{2}$
5 $\frac{3}{8}$
6 3 litres
7 56
8 198
9 990
10 21
11 54
12 30

13–18

Train departs at	Journey lasts	Train arrives at
09:30	40 minutes	**10:10**
09:42	30 minutes	10:12
10:45	**40 minutes**	11:25
11:15	50 minutes	**12:05**
11:40	40 minutes	12:20
12:35	**30 minutes**	13:05

19 1740
20 1800
21 2000
22 5
23 44
24 6 h 30 min
25 12
26 8
27 31
28 330
29 $\frac{1}{5}$
30 25
31 10
32 slow
33 15
34 fast
35 20
36 slow

37–41

×	4	6	8
3	12	**18**	24
5	20	30	**40**
7	**28**	42	56

42–47

×	3	7	5
7	21	49	
6		42	30
4	12		20

48 4.55
49 0.45
50 7.60

Paper 21

1 ×
2 −
3 +
4 ×
5 ÷
6 +
7 15.70
8 3.14
9 18
10 1570
11 30
12 101 000
13 189
14 19
15 26
16 5994
17 238 000
18 16

19–22

	Length	Width	Perimeter
Rectangle 1	7 m	5 m	**24** m
Rectangle 2	6 m	**4** m	20 m
Rectangle 3	**8** m	3 m	22 m
Rectangle 4	8 m	**5** m	26 m

23 30
24 Art
25 PE
26 1
27 17
28 13
29 6:14
30 6:28
31 6:49
32 12.78
33 23.776
34 431.2
35 1.243
36 21.34
37 3421 or 3421.0
38 1.043
39 24
40 $\frac{1}{8}$
41 10
42 1
43 3
44 5200
45 780
46 2480
47 9500
48 8400
49 13 180
50 2.9

Paper 22

1 20
2 21
3 23
4 $\frac{1}{2}$
5 $\frac{3}{8}$
6 $\frac{1}{4}$
7 37
8 27
9 26
10 August 27
11 September 26
12 October 25
13 84
14 80
15 76
16 144
17 8
18 11
19 7
20 11
21 17
22 Impossible
23 Certain
24 Likely
25 Unlikely
26 Equally likely
27 £5
28 2.222
29 2.22
30 2.2
31 2.12
32 2.02
33 1.87
34 26.07
35 3733.2
36 326
37 Moscow
38 Prague
39 Cape Town
40 29°C
41 Prague
42 Moscow
43 Cape Town
44 28°C
45 Prague
46–47 Cape Town, Glasgow
48 11:04
49 50
50 86

Paper 23

1 20
2 7
3 8
4 10 989
5 14
6 11
7 26
8 b
9 o
10 x
11 18.74
12 173
13 75.6
14 5.76
15 765 or 765.0
16 675 or 675.0
17 5.67
18 65.7
19 10
20 5
21 22:00
22 19:30 or 7:30 p.m.
23 >
24 <
25 0.433
26 0.008
27 1.73
28 310
29 261
30 17:49
31 27 m
32 9 m
33 $\frac{1}{3}$
34 12
35 16
36 23 400
37 47 900
38 35 200
39 77 100
40 19 200
41 3
42 96
43 $\frac{1}{4}$
44 1008
45 529
46 478
47 14
48–50 13, 14, 15

Paper 24

1–6

×	(4)	(7)	(5)
(2)	8	14	10
(9)	36	63	45
(1)	4	7	5

7 315
8–10 27, 36, 45
11 16
12 32
13 35
14 14
15 36
16 60
17 7.5

18 1.5
19 777
20 0.0777
21 27
22 1
23 34.16
24 6804
25 91
26 1 h 29 min
27 1 h 45 min
28 Train C
29 27

30 350
31 275
32 175
33 225
34 $1\frac{2}{5}$
35 $1\frac{1}{8}$
36 $1\frac{1}{2}$
37 $1\frac{2}{3}$
38 $1\frac{3}{5}$
39 $5\frac{1}{2}$
40 0.22

41 0.44
42 10
43 50
44 30

45–50

	A	B
Number of faces	6	7
Number of vertices	8	10
Number of edges	12	15

Change these fractions into percentages.

41 $\frac{20}{40}$ = _____

42 $\frac{5}{25}$ = _____

43 $\frac{40}{40}$ = _____

44 $\frac{20}{25}$ = _____

45 $\frac{10}{40}$ = _____

46 $\frac{15}{25}$ = _____

B 10
B 12

6

47–50 What numbers will come out of the machine?

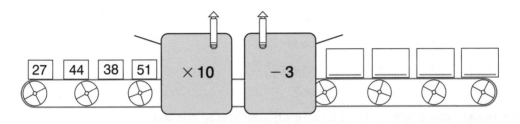

B 9

4

Now go to the Progress Chart to record your score! **Total** 50

Paper 13

1–4 Reflect these shapes in the mirror lines.

B 24

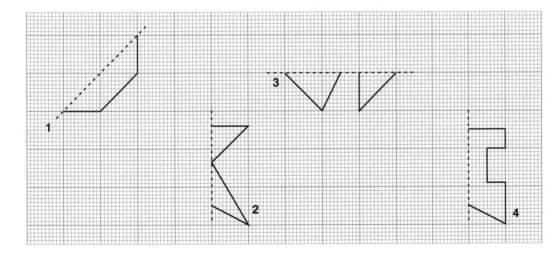

4

The sum of two numbers is 31.

5 If one number is 15, what is the other number?   _____

B 2

1

The children in Class 4 drew this pictogram to show where they live.

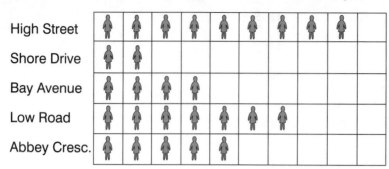

High Street										
Shore Drive										
Bay Avenue										
Low Road										
Abbey Cresc.										

Key

represents one child

6 How many children live in the High Street? _____

7 How many children live in Abbey Crescent? _____

8 How many children live in Shore Drive? _____

9 How many more children live in Low Road than in Bay Avenue? _____

10 What fraction of the class lives in the High Street? _____

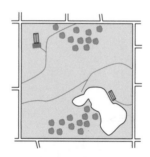

11 What is the area of a square park whose sides are 3 km? Choose the correct units from: cm, cm², m, m², m³, km, km². _____

12 What is the perimeter of the park? _____

13 If the area of another square park is 16 km², what is the length of one side? Choose the correct units from: cm, cm², m, m², m³, km, km². _____

14 What is the perimeter of this park? _____

Use this calculation to help you answer those below.

$$
\begin{array}{r}
98 \\
+\ 76 \\
\hline
174 \\
\hline
\end{array}
$$

15
$$
\begin{array}{r}
198 \\
+\ 176 \\
\hline
\end{array}
$$

16
$$
\begin{array}{r}
398 \\
+\ 76 \\
\hline
\end{array}
$$

17
$$
\begin{array}{r}
498 \\
+\ 176 \\
\hline
\end{array}
$$

B 14
B 10
B 2
5
B 20
4
B 2
3

18–21 Circle the **polygons** which show a correct axis of symmetry.

B 19
B 24

A B C D

E F G H

4

Fill in the missing figures.

B27/B25

22 5 minutes × _____ = 1 hour

23 20 cm × _____ = 1 metre

24 125 ml × _____ = 1 litre

25 50 m × _____ = 1 km

4

B 17

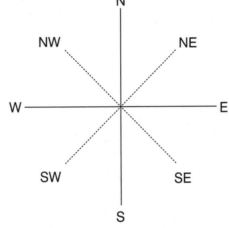

26 What is the size of the smaller angle between N and E? _____

27 How many degrees are there between N and S? _____

28 What is the size of the smaller angle between SE and W? _____

3

What number does the symbol represent in each question?

B 8

29 11 × (■ + 1 + 2) = 88   ■ = _____

30 21 ÷ (♠ − 2) = 3   ♠ = _____

31 4 + 3 × ● = 22   ● = _____

32 17 − ♠ × 2 = 7   ♠ = _____

33 ♦ × 4 + 3 = 39   ♦ = _____

34 (7 − ♣) × 5 + 9 = 29   ♣ = _____

6

35 My alarm clock loses a minute a day. If I put it right at noon on Monday, what time will it show at noon on Thursday? _____

B 27

1

B 6

36 Multiply 20 by itself. _____

37 Which number, when multiplied by itself, gives 169? _____

2

B 27

38 How many weeks in 161 days? _____

39 How many weeks in 378 days? _____

2

Scale: 1 cm represents 30 m

Give the answers to each of the following questions in metres.

B 26

40 How long is the church? _____

41–42 The churchyard is _____ long and _____ wide.

43 School Lane is _____ wide.

44–45 The school is _____ long and _____ wide.

46–47 The playground is _____ long and _____ wide.

8

48 The bus was due at 11:49 a.m. It arrived at 12:06 p.m. It was _____ minutes late.

B 27

49 Tom delivers newspapers from Monday to Saturday. If he delivers 49 each day, how many does he deliver in a week? _____

B 3

50 If it takes him 40 minutes each day, how long does he spend delivering papers each week? _____ hours

B27/B3

3

Now go to the Progress Chart to record your score! **Total** 50

Paper 14

Write TRUE or FALSE to the following:

1 $(245 \times 10) > (24 \times 100)$ _____ **2** $(2.45 \times 100) < (24 \times 10)$ _____

3 $(24.5 \times 10) < (2.4 \times 100)$ _____ **4** $(0.245 \times 100) > (24 \times 10)$ _____

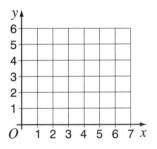

5–8 Plot and label the points A (0, 6), B (3, 0), C (4, 0), D (7, 6). Join up the points.

9 Is this a quadrilateral or a pentagon? _____

10 What is the special name for this shape? _____

11 Draw all the diagonals in the shape.

12 How many lines of symmetry does it have? _____

A cranberry juice concentrate needs 5 parts of water to every 1 part of concentrate.

13 How many litres of juice can you make with $\frac{1}{2}$ litre of concentrate? _____

A piece of rope, 2.34 m long, is cut into 9 equal pieces.

14 How long is each piece? Give your answer in centimetres. _____

Give each answer as a **mixed number** in their lowest terms.

15 $3 - 1\frac{9}{10} =$ _____ **16** $5 - 2\frac{1}{7} =$ _____

Write how many halves there are in:

17 $2\frac{1}{2}$ _____ **18** 4 _____ **19** $3\frac{1}{2}$ _____

20 $5\frac{1}{2}$ _____ **21** 3 _____ **22** $7\frac{1}{2}$ _____

Write the following fractions as decimals.

23 $\frac{23}{100}$ _____ **24** $\frac{17}{100}$ _____ **25** $\frac{30}{100}$ _____ **26** $\frac{9}{100}$ _____

Put these numbers in descending order:

27–31   21 484   216 486   21 426   216 824   21 648.6

_____ _____ _____ _____

32 Add half 28 to twice 19. _____ B2/B3

33 Write in figures the number ten thousand and fourteen. _____ B 1

34 How many times can I take 12 from 324? _____ B2/B3

35 The distance all round a square is 3.4 m. How long is each side in centimetres? _____ B 20

4

A show started at 19:30. $1\frac{1}{4}$ hours after this there was a 10-minute interval. B 27

36 When did the interval end? _____

37 If the second half of the show was the same length as the first half, when did the show end? _____

2

The sum of two numbers is 26 and their difference is 8. B2/B3

38 What is the larger number? _____   **39** The smaller number is _____

2

B14/B2
B15/B10

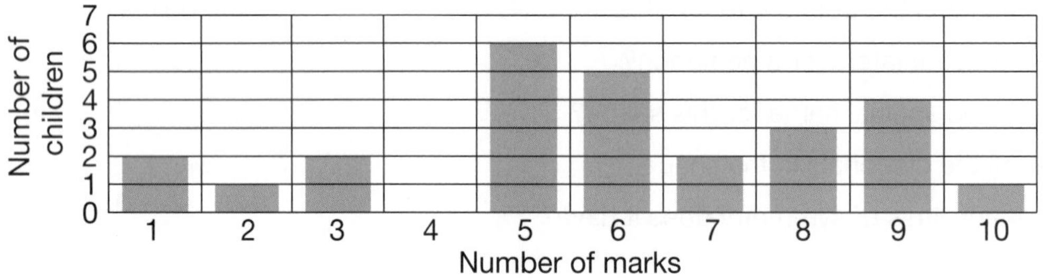

This bar chart shows how many marks 30 children got in a maths test.

40 How many children got 10 marks? _____

41 How many children got more than 7 marks? _____

42 How many children got 5–7 marks inclusive? _____

43 How many children got fewer than 4 marks? _____

44 How many children are shown on the bar chart? _____

45 Draw on the bar chart the number of children who got 4 marks. _____

46 What mark is the **mode**? _____

47 What fraction of the children got 8 or 9 marks? _____

48 What fraction of the children got 2 marks? _____

9

49 What is the smallest number which can be divided by both 5 and 7 without a remainder? _____ B 5

50 It rained on 19 days in January. How many days was it fine that month? _____ B 27

2

Now go to the Progress Chart to record your score!   **Total**   **50**

36

Paper 15

Change these into **mixed numbers** in their lowest terms.

1 $\frac{13}{10}$ _____

2 $\frac{7}{5}$ _____

3 $\frac{8}{3}$ _____

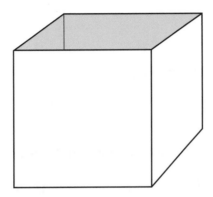

Here are some nets. Some will make an open cube (like the one shown above) and some will not.

Answer either TRUE or FALSE for each. (The black square is the base.)

4 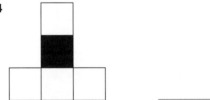 _____

5  _____

6  _____

7 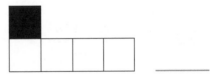 _____

8 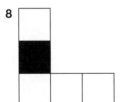 _____

What number needs to go in the box?

9 $7488 = 7000 + 400 + $ ☐ $ + 8$

10 $2341 = 2000 + 300 + 40 + $ ☐

What needs to be added/subtracted to change:

11 5864 to 7864? _____

12 9513 to 9313? _____

What are each of these numbers to the nearest 1000?

13 7680 _____

14 4535 _____

The product of two numbers is 56. One number is 7.

15 What is the other number? _____

Here is part of a centimetre ruler. Give your answer in centimetres.

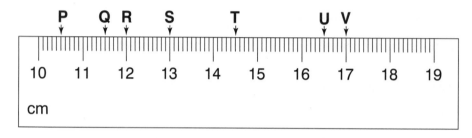

16 From P to Q is _____   17 From P to T is _____

18 From Q to U is _____   19 From R to U is _____

20 From S to U is _____   21 From T to V is _____

22 17)‾952‾   23 9191
                       −1717
                       _____

24   145
      × 308
      _____

25 78.05
     9.92
   + 5.07
   _____

Change the following into **improper fractions**.

26 $3\frac{1}{3}$ _____   27 $4\frac{1}{2}$ _____

28 $1\frac{3}{4}$ _____   29 $1\frac{1}{6}$ _____

30 $2\frac{1}{5}$ _____   31 $4\frac{2}{3}$ _____

Indicate which is larger by writing < or > in each space.

32 £13.07 _____ £13.60

33 €9.90 _____ €9.78

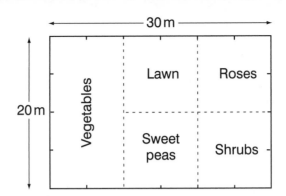

34 What is the area of the garden? _____

35 What fraction of the garden is used for growing vegetables? _____

36 What fraction of the garden is the rose bed? _____

37 What is the area of the shrubbery? _____

38 What is the perimeter of the garden? _____

Using all of the digits 5, 2, 6, 3 and 1, once only make:

39 the smallest number. _____

40 the smallest odd number. _____

41 the largest number. _____

42 the largest even number. _____

43–44 Draw the line of symmetry in each figure.

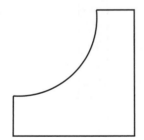

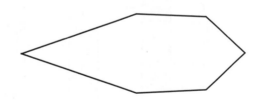

Write the following fractions as percentages.

45 $\frac{7}{10}$ = _____   **46** $\frac{10}{50}$ = _____

47 $\frac{10}{20}$ = _____   **48** $\frac{5}{20}$ = _____

49 $\frac{20}{50}$ = _____   **50** $\frac{40}{50}$ = _____

5

B 1

4

B 24

2

B 10
B 12

6

Now go to the Progress Chart to record your score!   Total   50

Paper 16

Write the next two numbers in each of the following lines.

1–2 77   88   99   _____   _____

3–4 $3\frac{1}{4}$ $3\frac{1}{2}$ $3\frac{3}{4}$ _____   _____

5–6 987   98.7   9.87   _____   _____

7
$$
\begin{array}{r}
7.69 \\
4.82 \\
+\ 3.68 \\
\hline
\end{array}
$$

8
$$
\begin{array}{r}
4.12 \\
-\ 2.76 \\
\hline
\end{array}
$$

9
$$
\begin{array}{r}
6.17 \\
\times\quad 8 \\
\hline
\end{array}
$$

10 $8\overline{)\,27.92}$

Here is a bar chart to show the number of people who came to see our school play.

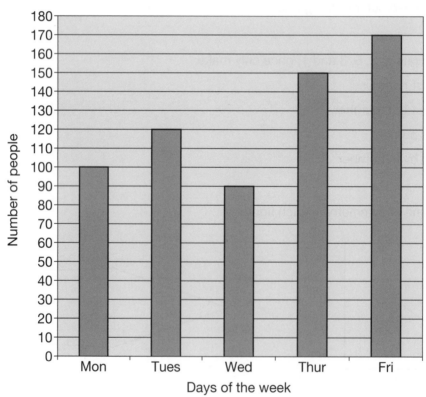

How many people came on:

11 Monday?   _____

12 Wednesday?   _____

13 What was the least popular day?   _____

14 The total audience was   _____

Indicate which is larger by writing $<$ or $>$ in each space.

15 5.001 m _____ 5.01 m

16 6.99 km _____ 6.099 km

17 What is the area of a floor 2.5 m × 3.5 m? _____

18 If the area of a room is 14 m² and the length is 4 m, what is the width? _____

19 Take four hundred and thirty-nine from seven thousand five hundred. Write the answer in figures. _____

Fill in the missing numbers.

20 3 × 4 × ♣ = 24   ♣ = _____

21 (8 ÷ 2) + ♥ = 10   ♥ = _____

22 ♠ + 7 + 3 = 12   ♠ = _____

23 4 × ● = 10 + 6   ● = _____

24–25 A room has a perimeter of 18 m. It is twice as long as it is wide.

It is _____ long and _____ wide.

Divide these numbers by 100.

26 3.55 _____

27 3.05 _____

28 30.5 _____

29 303.5 _____

30 3050 _____

31 40 × 0.02 = _____

32 70 × 1.1 = _____

33 Add $\frac{1}{4}$ of 48 to twice 19. _____

34 How many times can I take 39 from 624? _____

35 How much time is there between 11:45 p.m. on Wednesday and 5:27 a.m. on Thursday? _____ h _____ min

	David	Steven	Jerzy	Min
Maths	77	78	81	84
English	83	74	65	81
Geography	81	92	68	76
Science	69	68	49	77
Totals				

36–39 Write each child's total in the table.

A6/B25
2
B 20
2
B 2
1
B 8
4
B 20
2
B 1
5
B 11
2
B10/B2
B2/B3
B 27
3
B2/B15
4

40 Who had the most marks? _____

41 Who had the highest mark in any one exam? _____

42 Who had the lowest mark in any one exam? _____

43 What was the **range** of David's marks? _____

44 Who had the lowest **range** of marks? _____

45 What mark was the **mode** for all subjects? _____ ⬭ 6

B 20

46 What is the area of a square length 11 cm? _____ cm²

47 What is the perimeter of a rectangle with length 9.5 cm and width 13 cm? _____ cm ⬭ 2

Class 1 have 2000 beads in a box.

$\frac{1}{5}$ are red, 30% are blue and the rest are yellow.

B10/B12

48–50 There are _____ blue beads, _____ red beads and _____ yellow beads. ⬭ 3

Now go to the Progress Chart to record your score! **Total** ⬭ 50

Paper 17

B 2

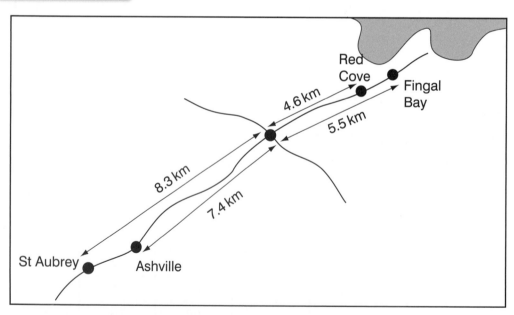

1 How far is it from Red Cove to St Aubrey? _____

2 How far is it from Ashville to Red Cove? _____

3 How far is it from Fingal Bay to St Aubrey? _____

4 How far is it from Ashville to Fingal Bay? _____ ⬭ 4

Underline the questions which have a remainder of 3.

5–6 $29 \div 5$ $21 \div 6$ $19 \div 4$ $28 \div 7$

7–8 $24 \div 7$ $77 \div 11$ $40 \div 12$ $27 \div 8$

9 If there are 20 lines on each page, on which page will the 110th line appear? _____

10 Rob had 52 battle game cards. He lost 16, then won back twice as many as he had lost.

How many has he got now? _____

The children in our class made this pie chart to show our favourite types of TV programmes.

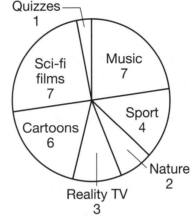

11 How many children prefer sci-fi films? _____

12–13 Which two types of TV programme are the **modes**? _____ and _____

14 What fraction of the class, in **lowest terms** prefer nature programmes? _____

15–16 Which two groups together number the same as those who like cartoons? _____ and _____

17 What percentage of the class prefer reality TV? _____

18 What percentage of the class prefer cartoons? _____

Double the following amounts.

19 £3.45 _____

20 $3\frac{3}{4}$ kg _____

Halve the following amounts.

21 912 _____   **22** £5.20 _____

I gave Tanya half of my chocolates and was left with 37.

23 How many did I have to start with? _____

43

99 is the same as **100 − 1**

24 367 + 99 = _____   25 744 + 99 = _____

26 468 + 99 = _____   27 702 + 99 = _____

28 Take one hundred and seventy-seven from ten thousand. _____

29 How many 24p stamps can I buy with £6.00? _____

In a class of 30 children one-tenth do *not* have school dinners.

  30 How many do have them? _____

We bought 120 cakes for a party. 27 were left.

  31 How many were eaten? _____

  32 Divide the following and write the answer as a decimal.

$$7\overline{)\,319.2}$$ _____

33 What is the perimeter of a room 4.7 m long and 3.5 m wide? _____

34 How much less than 20 m is the answer to question 33? _____

35–37 Plot and label the points A (1, 1), B (1, 4), C (4, 4).

      These are three **vertices** of a square ABCD.

38 Plot the other **vertex** (point) D and join the points.

39 Reflect the square in the mirror line.

40 Draw all the diagonals in the reflected square.

41 Translate the starting square 3 to the right.

42–45 Draw all the lines of symmetry in the translated
       square.

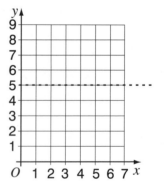

Write these times as they appear on a 24-hour digital clock.

46 Half past 7 in the morning ___ : ___   47 Quarter to 11 in the morning ___ : ___

48 Quarter past ten at night ___ : ___

49 Share £6.65 equally among 19 boys. Each boy has _____

50 345 × 300 _____

Paper 18

Write the following decimals as fractions in their **lowest terms**.

1 0.4 _____

2 0.25 _____

3 0.9 _____

4 0.03 _____

5 0.01 _____

6 0.07 _____

Find the area of each shape.

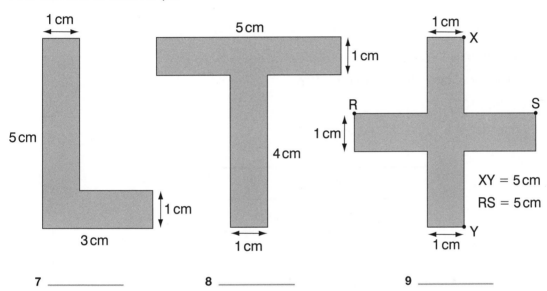

7 _____

8 _____

9 _____

10 How many 69p stamps can you buy for £13.80? _____

What is:

11 $6^2 + 11^2$? _____

12 $9^2 + 2^2$? _____

13 $8^2 + 12^2$? _____

14–17 The pairs of **factors** of 27 are: _____ and _____, _____ and _____

18–23 The pairs of **factors** of 16 are: _____ and _____, _____ and _____, _____ and _____

Together Tim, Simon and Rob have 35 computer games.

Simon has half as many as Tim, and Tim has half as many as Rob.

24–26 Rob has _____ computer games, Tim has _____ computer games and Simon has

_____.

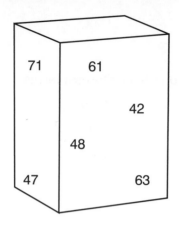

Which number above:

27 can be divided exactly by 7 and 6? _____

28 has a remainder of one when divided by 12? _____

29 is 52 less than 100? _____

30 has a remainder of 5 when divided by 11? _____

4

£1 = 1.53 US dollars
£1 = 121 Kenyan shillings
£1 = 1.23 euros
£1 = 1.72 Australian dollars

31 How many US dollars do you get for £200? $ _____

32 How many Kenyan shillings do you get for £5?   _____ shillings

33 How many pounds do you get for 172 Australian dollars?   £ _____

34 How many pounds do you get for 24.6 euros?   £ _____

4

35
```
  9.420
− 7.860
───────
```

36
```
  4.68
  9.25
+ 3.79
──────
```

37
```
  6.54
×    9
──────
```

38
```
  9.500
+ 6.750
───────
```

4

39 Draw lines between sets of equal values.

(9 × 12)	(4 × 50)
(11 × 11)	(9 × 11)
(20 × 10)	(120 + 1)
(102 − 3)	(110 − 2)

1

Write whether each angle is **acute**, **obtuse** or a right angle.

B 17

40 _____

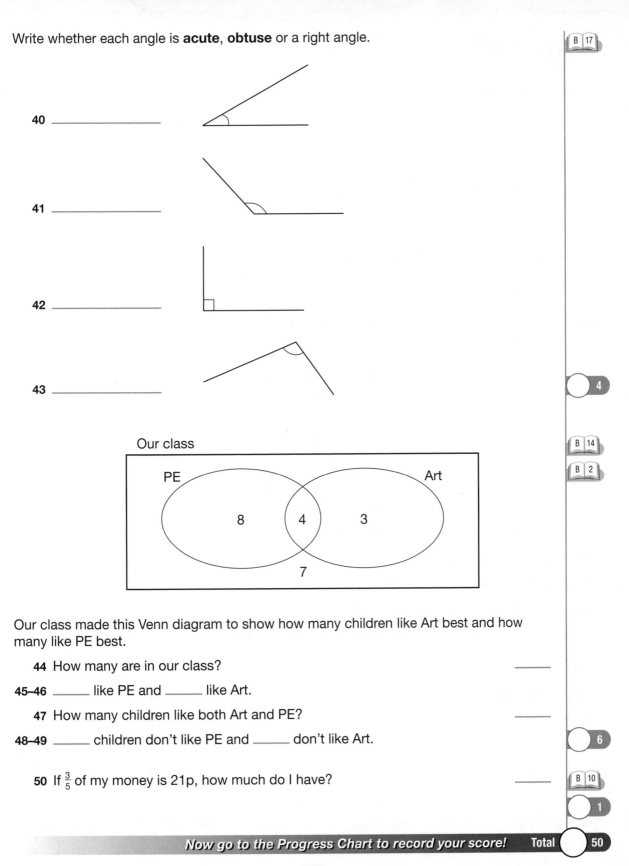

41 _____

42 _____

43 _____

4

B 14

B 2

Our class

PE ⬭ 8 ⬭ 4 ⬭ 3 ⬭ Art

7

Our class made this Venn diagram to show how many children like Art best and how many like PE best.

44 How many are in our class? _____

45–46 _____ like PE and _____ like Art.

47 How many children like both Art and PE? _____

48–49 _____ children don't like PE and _____ don't like Art.

6

50 If $\frac{3}{5}$ of my money is 21p, how much do I have? _____

B 10

1

Now go to the Progress Chart to record your score! Total 50

47

Paper 19

Complete these questions by filling in the missing numbers.

1 $\dfrac{}{3} = \dfrac{16}{24}$

2 $\dfrac{11}{12} = \dfrac{}{48}$

3 $\dfrac{7}{10} = \dfrac{}{60}$

4 $\dfrac{}{7} = \dfrac{8}{28}$

5 $\dfrac{}{9} = \dfrac{20}{36}$

6 $\dfrac{8}{9} = \dfrac{}{54}$

B 10

6

7–8 Which two consecutive numbers add up to 17? _____ and _____

B2/B6

2

9 How many seconds are there in 20 minutes 28 seconds? _____

B 27

1

Here is a chart which shows the *height* in centimetres of each of my friends.

B 26

B 2

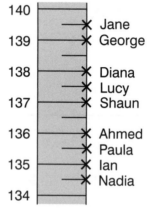

```
140 ─┬──
     │   ──✕ Jane
139 ─┤   ──✕ George
     │
138 ─┤   ──✕ Diana
     │   ──✕ Lucy
137 ─┤   ──✕ Shaun
     │
136 ─┤   ──✕ Ahmed
     │   ──✕ Paula
135 ─┤   ──✕ Ian
     │   ──✕ Nadia
134 ─┴──
```

10 How much taller is Jane than Lucy? _____

11 How much taller is George than Paula? _____

12 How much shorter is Ian than Lucy? _____

13 What is the difference in height between Shaun and Nadia? _____

4

Fill in the missing numbers.

B 8

14 $(4 + 7) \times (\bullet - 3) = 99$ $\bullet$ = _____

15 $\spadesuit \div 7 + 3 = 6$ $\spadesuit$ = _____

16 $\blacksquare + (6 \div 3) \times 2 = 6$ $\blacksquare$ = _____

17 $(5 \times \clubsuit) + (\clubsuit \times 2) + 6 = 27$ $\clubsuit$ = _____

4

B 25

18 0.25 m = _____ cm

19 0.5 kg = _____ g

20 1 km = _____ m

21 346 cm = _____ m

22 12.2 cm = _____ mm

23 2.5 kg = _____ g

6

Answer TRUE or FALSE to the following.

24 4.7 metres < 468 cm _____

25 22 minutes > $\frac{2}{5}$ hour _____

26–34 Complete the table.

A   B   C

	A	B	C
Number of **faces**			
Number of **vertices**			
Number of **edges**			

35 $(3 \times \clubsuit) + 2 = 26$ $\clubsuit$ = _____   **36** $(\heartsuit \times 2) - 2 = 26$ $\heartsuit$ = _____

37 $(4 \times \spadesuit) - 2 = 34$ $\spadesuit$ = _____   **38** $(2 \times \bullet) - 5 = 9$ $\bullet$ = _____

Underline the correct answer for each line.

39 $\frac{1}{2} \times \frac{1}{2}$ = $\frac{1}{4}$ $\frac{1}{8}$ $\frac{1}{2}$ 1   2

40 0.1×0.1 =   0.2   0.02   0.1   0.01   0.11

41 $4 \div \frac{1}{4}$ =   1   4   16   2 $\frac{1}{4}$

42 $2 - 0.1$ =   1.1   1.9   2.1   0.9   1.2

43 $1 + 0.1 + 0.01$ =   2.1   1.2   2.01   1.101   1.11

44 $\frac{1}{2}$ of 66   =   60   66   30   33   25

45 If Phil can swim 15 m in 20 seconds, how far can he swim,
at the same speed, in 2 minutes? _____

46 If it takes Maria a quarter of an hour to walk to school,
what time must she leave home to get to school by 8:50 a.m.? _____

47 How many books, each 1.2 cm thick, can be stood on a shelf
50.4 cm wide? _____

48 What is the **range** of these numbers?   4   8   3   9   _____

49–50 In a school there are 200 pupils. $\frac{2}{5}$ of them are girls.

There are _____ girls and _____ boys.

Now go to the Progress Chart to record your score!   Total   50

Paper 20

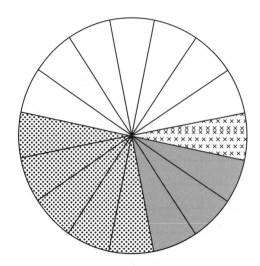

B 10

What fraction of the circle is: (Remember to express fractions in the lowest terms)

1 dotted? _____   **2** grey? _____   **3** unshaded? _____

4 What fraction of the circle is dotted and grey? _____

5 What fraction has crosses and dots? _____

5

6 An orange juice concentrate needs 4 parts of water to every 1 part of concentrate. How many litres of juice can you make with 0.6 litres of concentrate? _____

B 13

7 What number is halfway between 45 and 67? _____

B 2

2

8–9 Look at the number 1212.

What is the difference in the value of:

the two 2s? _____   the two 1s? _____

B 1

2

10 Add half of 18 to twice 6. _____

B 2

11 Twice a number is 36. What is three times the number? _____

B 3

2

12 Laura ate four-fifths of her sweets. If she had 6 left, how many had she at first? _____

B 10

1

13–18 Complete the following table.

Train departs at	Journey lasts	Train arrives at
09.30	40 minutes	_____
_____	30 minutes	10:12
10.45	_____	11:25
11:15	50 minutes	_____
_____	40 minutes	12:20
12:35	_____	13:05

6

What is the next number after 1738 which:

B 1

19 ends in a zero? _____   **20** ends in two zeros? _____

3

21 ends in three zeros? _____

22 I think of a number, add 1, divide by 3, and the answer is 2.

B2/B3

What is the number? _____

1

In my sister's box of counters, 50% of them are green, 25% are blue and there are 11 white counters.

B 12

23 How many counters are there altogether? _____

1

24 How long will it take a lorry to go 325 km at a constant speed of 50 km/h? _____ h _____ min

B 3

1

The sum of the ages of Anita and Peter is 20 years.

B2/B3

25–26 Anita is 4 years older than Peter.   Anita is _____ and Peter is _____ .

2

The difference between two numbers is 14. The smaller number is 17.

B 2

27 What is the other number? _____

1

In a village of 550 people, 40% of the population are adults.

B12/B2

28 How many children are there? _____

1

29 In a test, 24 out of 30 children passed. What fraction failed? Give in your answer in **lowest terms**. _____

B 10

30 How many times can I take 5 from 125? _____

B2/B3

2

The correct time is 5 past 10. How fast or slow are these clocks?

Write the number of minutes and cross out the words that are not needed.

31–32 _____ minutes   fast

                                  slow

33–34 _____ minutes   fast

                                  slow

35–36 _____ minutes   fast

                                  slow

Fill in the missing numbers in these multiplication tables.

37–41

×	4	_____	8
3	12	_____	24
_____	20	30	_____
7	_____	42	56

5

42–47

×	_____	_____	_____
_____	21	49	
_____		42	30
_____	12		20

I bought 7 toys at 65p each.

  48 How much did they cost?   £ _____

  49 How much change would I have out of £5.00?   £ _____

  50 My aunt said she would give my sister 40p for every complete kilometre
        she walked. She walked 19.5 km. How much money did she receive?   £ _____

Now go to the Progress Chart to record your score!   Total   50

Paper 21

Insert a sign in each space to make each question correct.

1–2 3 _____ 4 = 13 _____ 1

3–4 8 _____ 1 = 3 _____ 3

5–6 10 _____ 2 = 4 _____ 1

| £1 = 1.2 euros |
| £1 = 1.57 Canadian dollars |

7 How many Canadian dollars do you get for £10? $ _____

8 How many Canadian dollars do you get for £2? $ _____

9 How many euros do you get for £15?   € _____

10 How many Canadian dollars do you get for £1000? $ _____

11 How many euros do you get for £25?   € _____

12 Write in figures the number: one hundred and one thousand.   _____

13 What number, when divided by 11, has an answer 17 remainder 2?   _____

14–15 The sum of two numbers is 45, and their difference is 7.

The smaller number is _____ and the larger is _____ .

16	7001	**17**	476
	− 1007		× 500

18 I think of a number, divide it by 4 and then add 2. The answer is 6. What is the number?   _____

19–22 Complete the following table.

	Length	**Width**	**Perimeter**
Rectangle 1	7 m	5 m	_____ m
Rectangle 2	6 m	_____ m	20 m
Rectangle 3	_____ m	3 m	22 m
Rectangle 4	8 m	_____ m	26 m

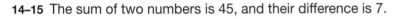

The children in our class made this pie chart which shows our favourite lessons.

Favourite lesson

Craft 6, Art 10, PE 9, Singing 5

23 How many children are there in the class? _____

24 What lesson is the **mode**? _____

25 What is the next most popular lesson? _____

26 How many more children prefer craft than prefer singing? _____

27 There are 4 more boys than girls in the class. How many boys are there? _____

28 How many girls are there in the class? _____

My watch gains 7 minutes a day. If I put it right at 6 p.m. on Sunday, what time will it show:

29 at 6 p.m. on Tuesday? _____ p.m.

30 at 6 p.m. on Thursday? _____ p.m.

31 at 6 p.m. the following Sunday? _____ p.m.

32 Take 22 cm from 13 m. _____ m

33 Add together 9 kg, 276 g and 14.5 kg. _____ kg

34–38 Put a decimal point in these numbers so that the 1 will have the value of 1 unit.

    4 3 1 2   1 2 4 3   2 1 3 4   3 4 2 1   1 0 4 3

Our class made this bar chart, which shows our favourite pets.

54

39 How many children are there in our class? _____

40 What fraction of the class prefers rabbits? _____

41 How many children prefer dogs? _____

42 How many children like hamsters best? _____

43 How many more children like dogs than like cats? _____

5

Here is a table showing some approximate distances in km between different airports in the world.

B 14
B 2

	London	Paris	Moscow	New York	Hong Kong	Montreal
London		340	2500	5900	9500	5200
Paris	340		2480	6150	9600	5500
Moscow	2500	2480		7800	7100	7040
New York	5900	6150	7800		13 000	780
Hong Kong	9500	9600	7100	13 000		12 400
Montreal	5200	5500	7040	780	12 400	

44 London to Montreal is _____ km.   **45** New York to Montreal is _____ km.

46 Moscow to Paris is _____ km.   **47** Hong Kong to London is _____ km.

Give the total distance of a flight from:

48 New York to Moscow via London   _____ km

49 Hong Kong to New York via Montreal   _____ km

6

50 By how much is 3.5 greater than 0.6? _____

B 11
1

Now go to the Progress Chart to record your score!   Total   50

Paper 22

Write the next three terms in each of the following lines.

B 7

1–3   12   14   15   17   18   ____   ____   ____

4–6 $\frac{7}{8}$ $\frac{3}{4}$ $\frac{5}{8}$ ____   ____   ____

B 10

7–9   60   59   49   48   38   ____   ____   ____

10–12   May 30   June 29   July 28 _____   _____   _____

13–15   100   96   92   88   ____   ____   ____

15

The children in Brambledown School made this frequency table which shows their ages.

Age	Number of children
7	22
8	43
9	36
10	28
11	15

16 How many children are there in the school? _____

17 Which age group represents the **mode**? _____

18 Which age group is the smallest? _____

19 How many more children are there who are 8 than are 9? _____

20 If half the children who are 7 are boys, how many are girls? _____

21 If there are twenty-six 8-year-old boys, how many girls are 8? _____

CERTAIN   LIKELY   EQUALLY LIKELY   UNLIKELY   IMPOSSIBLE

Match one word or phrase to each of the statements below.

22 Next year there will be 55 Wednesdays. _____

23 The sun will set in the west tomorrow. _____

24 There are 365 days in any given year. _____

25 I will roll a number 5 with a fair dice. _____

26 I will roll a prime number with a fair dice. _____

27 Jane spent a quarter of her pocket money on a book, saved half of it, and spent the rest on sweets. If she spent £1.25 on sweets, how much did she have at first? _____

28–32 Arrange these decimals in order, putting the largest first.

2.02   2.2   2.222   2.12   2.22

_____   _____   _____   _____   _____

33 $\begin{array}{r} 9.25 \\ -\ 7.38 \\ \hline \end{array}$

34 $\begin{array}{r} 14.37 \\ +\ 11.70 \\ \hline \end{array}$

35 $\begin{array}{r} 612 \\ \times\ 6.1 \\ \hline \end{array}$

36 $21)\overline{6846}$

The temperature in five cities was recorded at noon on February 1st.

City	°C
Prague	−2
Cape Town	25
New York	−1
Glasgow	4
Moscow	−4

37 Where was the coldest place at noon on February 1st? _____

38 Where was the second coldest place at noon? _____

39 Where was the warmest place at noon? _____

40 What is the **range** of temperature at noon? _____

The temperatures were taken again at 11 p.m.

City	°C
Prague	−13
Cape Town	15
New York	−6
Glasgow	0
Moscow	−11

41 Where was the coldest place at 11 p.m. on February 1st? _____

42 Where was the second coldest place at 11 p.m.? _____

43 Where was the warmest place at 11 p.m.? _____

44 What is the **range** of temperature at 11 p.m.? _____

45 Where was the biggest drop in temperature between noon and 11 p.m. on February 1st? _____

46–47 Which cities never dropped below freezing?

_____ and _____

11

48 The train due at 10:53 was 11 minutes late. When did it arrive? ___ : ___

49 Add $\frac{1}{5}$ of 10 to twice 24. ___

2

50 Kirstie had 50 battle game cards. She lost 18 and then won back three times as many as she had lost.

How many has she got now? ___

1

Paper 23

Complete these fractions.

1 $\dfrac{2}{10} = \dfrac{4}{\quad}$ **2** $\dfrac{5}{5} = \dfrac{\quad}{7}$ **3** $\dfrac{3}{6} = \dfrac{4}{\quad}$

4 Take 11 from 11 thousand.   _____

5 If *Reallyclean* costs £2.80 for 5 litres, how much would I pay for $\frac{1}{4}$ litre?   _____ p

6 When I take 4 times a certain number from 50 the remainder is 6.
What is the number?   _____

7 The sum of two numbers is 43. The smaller number is 17.
What is the other number?   _____

Look at each set of letters below. They form a pattern.

8 a b b r a b b r ...   What would the 11th letter be?   _____

9 b y t o b y b y t ...   What would the 10th letter be?   _____

10 x x y z z x x y ...   What would the 16th letter be?   _____

11 What is the perimeter of a room which is 5.4 m long and 3.97 m wide?   _____ m

12 Take 347 centimetres from 5.2 metres.   _____ cm

13–18 Put a decimal point in these numbers so that the 5 will have the value of 5 units.

     7 5 6   5 7 6   7 6 5   6 7 5   5 6 7   6 5 7

Using this world time chart answer the questions below.

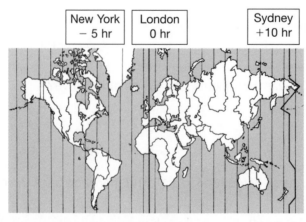

New York	London	Sydney
− 5 hr	0 hr	+10 hr

19 How many hours apart are London and Sydney?   _____

20 How many hours apart are London and New York?   _____

B 10

3

B1/B2

B10/B3

B2/B3

B 2

4

B 7

3

B 20

B25/B2

2

B 1

6

B 2

21 It is 12:00 midday in London. What does a digital clock in Sydney show? ___ : ___

22 It is 04:30 in New York. What time is it in Sydney? _____

A6/B25

Indicate which is larger by writing < or > in each space.

23 4100 m _____ 4.09 km

24 999 ml _____ 1.009 litre

B11/B3

25 Divide 86.6 by 200. _____

26 0.2 × 0.2 × 0.2 = _____

27 Find the product of 3.46 and 0.5. _____

28 How many times can I subtract 0.06 from 18.6? _____

B 2

29
```
    87
    65
    46
    38
  + 25
  ─────

  ─────
```

30 The train, which was 13 minutes late, arrived at 18:02.
When should it have arrived? _____

B 27

The perimeter of the church hall is 72 m. It is three times as long as it is wide.

B 20

31 What is its length? ___   **32** What is its width? ___

33 There are 8 brown dogs and 4 white dogs. What fraction of the dogs are
white? Write your answer in its **lowest terms**. _____

B 10

There are 28 children in a class. $\frac{3}{7}$ of them are boys.

B 10

34 How many boys are there? ___   **35** How many girls are there? ___

36–40 Round off these numbers to the nearest 100.

B 1

23 432	47 874	35 153	77 077	19 191
_____	_____	_____	_____	_____

41 Three numbers are multiplied together to make 360.
Two of the numbers are 12 and 10. What is the third number? ___

B 3

42 What is the sum of the odd numbers between 10 and 22? _____ B 2

43 In our class 12 girls have short hair, and 4 girls have long hair. What fraction of the girls have long hair? Write your answer in **lowest terms**. _____

B 10

3

Belford-on-Sea has a population of 2015. The men and women together number 1007, and the women and children together number 1537. How many:

B2/B3

44 children are there? _____   **45** women are there? _____

46 men are there? _____

3

47 The ages of Alison and Juma add up to 26 years. Alison is 2 years older than Juma so Alison is _____

B3/B2

1

48–50 Which three consecutive numbers add up to 42? _____ and _____ and _____

B3/B2

B 6

3

Now go to the Progress Chart to record your score!   **Total** ◯ **50**

Paper 24

1–6 Complete the brackets in this multiplication table. B 3

×	_____	_____	_____
_____	8	14	
_____		63	45
_____	4		5

6

7 How many days are there in 45 weeks? _____ B 27

8–10 Write down the numbers between 20 and 50 that are exactly divisible by 9. B 5

_____   _____   _____

4

Fill in the missing numbers in each line. B 7

11–12	12	_____	20	24	28	_____
13–14	_____	28	21	_____	7	
15–16	24	_____	48	_____	72	84
17–18	9	_____	6	4.5	3	_____
19–20	_____	77.7	7.77	0.777	_____	
21–22	81	_____	9	3	_____	

12

60

23   4.88
    × 7
    ───

24   756
    × 9
    ───

25 11) ‾‾‾‾‾
         1001

3

	Train A	Train B	Train C
Middlesbrough	11:35	13:20	14:35
Stockton	11:46	13:44	14:46
West Hartlepool	12:07	14:07	15:07
Sunderland	12:36	14:36	15:36
Newcastle	13:04	15:05	16:03

26 How long does Train A take to travel from Middlesbrough to Newcastle?

_____ h _____ min

27 How long does Train B take to do the same journey?   _____ h _____ min

28 Which is the fastest of the three trains?   _____

29 How long does Train C take to travel from Sunderland to Newcastle?

_____ minutes

4

Here is a pictogram which shows how many people went to the Cyber Café last week.
Use it to answer the questions.

Mon 👤 👤 👤 👤 ˥

Tues 👤 👤 👤 👤 👤 ˥

Wed 👤 👤 ˥

Thur 👤 👤 👤 👤 👤 👤

Fri 👤 👤 👤 👤 👤 👤 👤

Sat 👤 👤 👤 👤 👤 ˥

Key
👤 = 50 people

30 How many people visited on Friday?   _____

31 How many people visited on Tuesday?   _____

32 How many more people went to the café on Thursday than
Wednesday?   _____

33 What is the **range** of the number of people who visited each day?   _____

4

Write these **improper fractions** as **mixed numbers** in their lowest term.

34 $\frac{7}{5}$ = _____   **35** $\frac{9}{8}$ = _____

36 $\frac{3}{2}$ = _____   **37** $\frac{5}{3}$ = _____

38 $\frac{8}{5}$ = _____   **39** $\frac{11}{2}$ = _____

6

Write each fraction as a decimal.

40 $\frac{22}{100}$ ____

41 $\frac{22}{50}$ ____

B 11

2

Fill in the missing numbers.

42 $6 \times 7 \times$ ____ $= 420$

43 $2 \times 3 \times$ ____ $= 300$

44 $3 \times 4 \times$ ____ $= 360$

B 3

3

A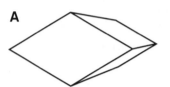

B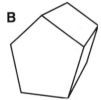

B 21

45–50 Complete the table.

	A	B
Number of faces		
Number of **vertices**		
Number of edges		

6

Now go to the Progress Chart to record your score! Total 50

62

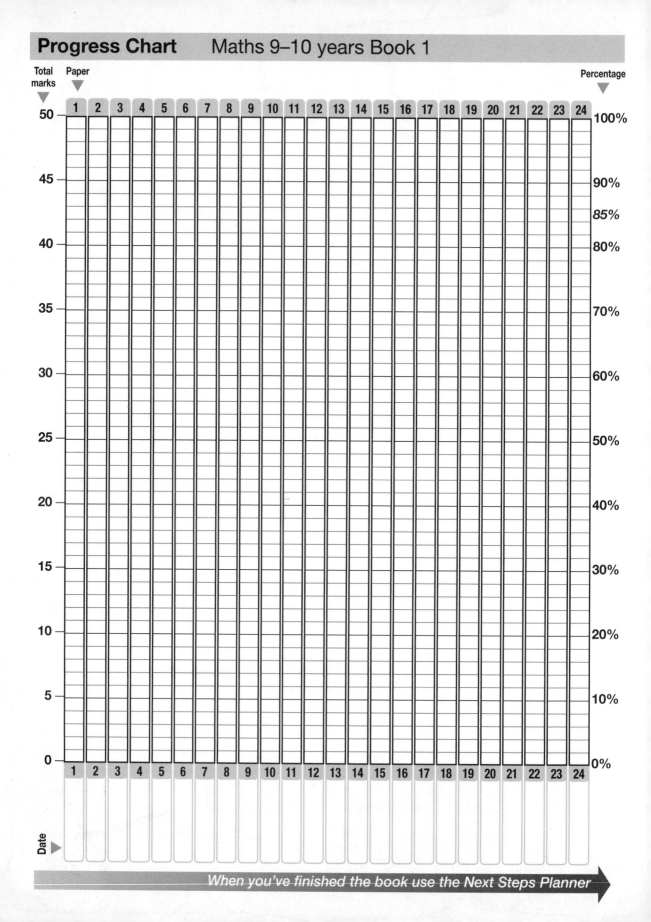